$1\frac{35}{x}$

UTOPIA

FROM THE FIRST EDITION OF THE *UTOPIA*

Frontispiece

UTOPIA

By
ST. THOMAS MORE

Translated by
RALPH ROBINSON

*Edited in Modern Spelling with Introduction and Notes
by the*
RIGHT REV. MGR PHILIP E. HALLETT

With a Foreword by
LORD RUSSELL OF KILLOWEN

LONDON
BURNS OATES & WASHBOURNE LTD
PUBLISHERS TO THE HOLY SEE

NIHIL OBSTAT:

ERNESTUS MESSENGER, PH.D.,
Censor deputatus.

IMPRIMATUR:

LEONELLUS CAN. EVANS,
Vic. Gen.

WESTMONASTERII,
die 25a Julii 1937.

MADE AND PRINTED IN GREAT BRITAIN
FOR
BURNS OATES & WASHBOURNE LTD
1937

FOREWORD

WHEN I was invited, and undertook, to write a layman's introduction to Monsignor Hallett's new edition of *Utopia* I consoled myself with the thought that the task would compel me to re-read a classic, and to sit once more on that bench ' covered with green turf ' in the Antwerp garden, listening in company with the future Saint and Peter Giles, to Raphael Hythloday, the old sunburnt traveller, describing the island of Utopia, and the manners and customs of its inhabitants—the imaginary island of ' Nowhere,' whose name has come to be synonymous with the impossible ideal.

This new edition may properly be called the first Catholic edition of an English translation of the *Utopia*, and the question not unnaturally suggests itself for consideration, How far is More's attitude towards various questions of social importance revealed in the work, and, so far as revealed, to what extent does it coincide with the views of Catholics to-day ?

The main difficulty encountered at the outset is to know how far More intended to put forward the views of Hythloday and the Utopians as views entertained and approved by himself. One thing I think is certain, that the old Seebohm view is exploded. It is difficult to understand how it was ever accepted. In the first book (in which at times

More joins in the conversation and gives his own views) we find a general statement that while Hythloday, in regard to those newly-discovered lands, rehearsed divers acts and constitutions whereby other countries could take example and amend their errors, he also marked ' many fonde and folisshe lawes' in those same lands. The second book is even more explicit in showing that the author disclaims wholesale approval of Utopian ideas. Many things in their manners and laws seemed, he says, ' to be instituted and founded of no good reason,' and chiefly in ' the principal foundation of all their ordinances that is to say in the communitie of their life and living.'

The old idea, however, still prevails at times. In a recent debate in the House of Lords upon a Bill for legalising forms of suicide and murder under the name of ' Euthanasia,' I heard the noble sponsor of the Bill claim St. Thomas More as a supporter of the measure. Truly a startling proposition to Catholics ! In time no doubt he will be cited as an opponent of clerical celibacy, and an advocate of a female ministry, because, according to Hythloday, in Utopia women were not excluded from the priesthood, and ' the men priestes take to their wifes the chiefest women in all their countreye.'

In truth St. Thomas More is engaged in depicting a community which though possessing some kind, or indeed many kinds, of religious views, is a non-Christian community which had not the advantage and guidance of the Catholic Faith. But it is also a community which, in spite of this deprivation, had succeeded in some respects in getting nearer to perfection than Catholic England.

Does England to-day compare more favourably with Utopia than she did when Utopia was written ? It is an interesting question, and one not easy to answer.

As the first book shows, the principal targets for Hythloday's indignation were the conversion of England's arable lands into pasture, and the infliction in England of the penalty of death for theft. He describes his discussion with the English lawyer at Cardinal Morton's table, and shows how capital punishment for theft ' passeth the limites of Justice,' and that the prevalence of theft is due to lack of instruction in handicrafts. Further that pasture kills husbandry ' which requireth manye hands.' These are discharged and thrown upon the world, and when they have wandered abroad and spent their small goods, ' what can they els doo but steale, and then justly pardy be hanged, or else go about a beggyng.' Whether agriculture receives or does not receive sufficient and proper encouragement in England to-day, may well be a moot point. Hythloday might still think that husbandry is killed. One thing, however, is quite certain ; it took England some three centuries to mitigate the severity of her criminal laws by abolishing capital punishment for theft. This does not, however, mean that throughout that time the sense of the country approved of the law. In fact it had long ceased to do so ; and juries had become accustomed to resort to findings of a most depreciatory character in relation to the value of articles alleged to be stolen, for the purpose of bringing the case below the statutory limit, and so freeing the prisoner from the scaffold. But the

English Statute Book remained as an object of scorn for the Utopian, and of shame to England until the early years of the nineteenth century. Then, and not before, would Hythloday have been appeased. Then, and not before, could England look Utopia in the face.

There is much in the first Book to give us food for thought nowadays. Hythloday asks how he would fare if he were to counsel a King to be content to rule his country for the benefit of his subjects, and not to meddle into other kingdoms. ' This myne advyse maister More,' he asks, ' how thinke you it would be harde and taken ? So, God help me not very thankfully, quod I.' Nor I fear would such a twentieth-century counsellor obtain in some quarters any more successful hearing, in these days of expanding empires, and places in the sun.

Means of enriching a ruler are indicated which display a not unfamiliar ingenuity. One counsellor suggests the appreciation of currency when payments have to be made, and its depreciation when payments are to be received. Another the raising of money under apprehension, feigned perhaps, of war. Another counsels the corruption of the judges, so that judicial decisions shall always be favourable to the Crown. That at least is inconceivable in England to-day. But what *is* true now, and has been true through the ages, is that a king's ' honoure and safetye is more and rather supported and upholden by the wealth and ryches of his people, than by hys owne treasures.' A prosperous people is a contented people, they have stakes in their country. Only those who have nothing to lose create insecurity : for ' who be bolder

stomaked to bring all in a burlieburlye (thereby
trusting to get some windfal) than they that have
now nothing to leese ? '

But how can such general prosperity be attained ?
Hythloday says, by community of goods. He cites
Utopia as an example of a country in which ' all
things being there common, everye man hath
aboundance of everye thing.' As Plato foresaw,
he says, this is ' the one and onlye waye to the
wealthe of a communaltye, if equalitye of all thinges
should be broughte in and stablyshed.' This More
challenges—' But I am of a contrary opinion (quod
I) for methinketh that men shal never live wealthelye,
where all things be commen.' But Hythloday again
cites Utopia to the contrary, and this leads, so to
speak, to the adjournment of the debate for dinner,
and to the detailed account of Utopia which is
contained in the second book.

Many matters which Hythloday tells concerning
the Utopians, are of great interest in relation to
present-day habits and experience. First and
foremost is the Communism of Utopia. The whole
island is one family or household, divided into
various units, the smaller or basic units being the
families of kinsfolk with a minimum of ten and a
maximum of sixteen children of the age of fourteen
years or thereabouts, all necessary adjustments
being made by transfers from one family to another.
Thirty families are ruled by a Philarche whose
chief duty it is to see that no one is idle. Ten
Philarches and their three hundred families are
under a Chief Philarche, and the Prince is chosen
by the Philarches. Each group of thirty families
has its common dining-hall. Everyone works for

the common good, be it in husbandry or other crafts and sciences, and since everyone works (or nearly everyone, for some for good reasons are exempted) there is no need for any to work unduly long hours. Indeed the hours of labour are restricted to six hours. In one passage it is stated that six hours are assigned to work before noon, when the people dine, and that they work for three hours between dinner and supper, and a little later on Hythloday says—' For seeing they bestowe but vi hours in worke, perchance you may think that the lacke of some necessarye thinges hereof may ensue. But this is nothinge so.' We have here the equivalent of the nineteenth-century eight hours working day, with its tendency to shorten under the stress of the 'post-haste and romage' of modern times.

All this describes a 'communism' admirable in theory, to which no objection could be taken, if it could be reproduced in fact as a voluntary system, and made to work. It is as ideal and as attractive as W. H. Mallock's *New Republic*, in which everyone honourably served the State by doing the particular work assigned to him by the State, and in which the crossing-sweeper earned as much honour and gratitude from his fellowmen for the work which he performed, as did the Prime Minister for the services which he rendered.

' Communism ' is a word which, from its association with various forms of governmental violence, has acquired sinister meanings. Nowadays it connotes to many, and with justification, antagonism to God and to religion; certainly antagonism to Catholicism and to its faith and practice. With such communism no Catholic, indeed no honest Christian, can have any dealing whatsoever. But the theory of Communism, viz. community of goods, if associated with religious tolerance and unassociated with any antagonism to God, is not necessarily inconsistent with Catholicism and attachment to that faith. But the abolition of private property must be voluntary and not compulsory. 'Every man has by nature the right to possess property as his own'; so said Pope Leo XIII in the *Rerum Novarum* Encyclical. That right must remain. Although St. Thomas More was sceptical as to the successful or practical operation of a system of common ownership, he might perhaps (had he ever subsequently talked with Hythloday as he hoped to do) have altered his views as to its practicability and yet have remained a sincere and devout Catholic. The Communism of Utopia, though compulsory, was certainly not anti-God or anti-religious. All views on religion could be privately entertained. All forms of religion could be openly professed and openly preached provided their tenets did not involve a disbelief in the existence of a Divine Providence, or in the immortality of the soul. Anyone harbouring such disbelief was not counted in the number of men, and was despised 'as of an unprofitable and of a base and vile nature.' He received no physical punishment, but was placed in a kind of moral Coventry.

How stood Utopia in regard to matrimony? In his earlier references Hythloday speaks of 'marriage wherein all the lyfe must be led with one,' but it is clear that divorce within limits was permissible. Adultery broke the bond and also whatever was covered by the words 'the intolerable wayward manners of either party.' The innocent party could remarry with leave of the Council, the guilty party could not, and was punished with most grievous bondage. The Council might allow a divorce for incompatibility, but only if both parties desired it. The Council, however, allowed no divorces without a careful examination and trial of the matter by themselves and their wives; and were loath to allow a divorce for the shrewd reason, ' because they know this to be the next way to break love between man and wife, to be in easy hope of a new marriage.' This limited recognition of divorce, subject to strict investigation, and involving stern consequences to an offending party, is a striking instance of More's indication of, not what he himself considered right, but how he thought a heathen state would act, guided simply by the pagan virtues, and unassisted by revealed religion. Nor can a Catholic fail to feel some admiration for the strictness with which the heathen Utopia of the sixteenth century regarded the marriage tie, when he thinks of the almost farcical laxity to which it has been reduced in this Christian country to-day.

The Utopians were to be envied in one respect. They had but few laws. Their views in this regard were eminently sound, for they thought it against all right and justice that men should be bound by laws which are not only too numerous to read, or else ' blinder and darker than that anye man can well understande them.' What a text for our legislators and parliamentary draftsmen to ponder over ! Not so attractive is the thought that all attorneys, proctors, and serjeants-at-law are banished from the island; still less attractive is the reason, that in Utopia 'every man is a cunning lawier.' To those who have had experience of litigants in person, the prospect of a nation entirely composed of them makes no appeal.

Their views on leagues and covenants have in these days of the League of Nations (with its shortage of members and its unenforceable covenant) a strangely Utopian ring. They would have no league or covenant, for, said they, 'the fellowship of nature is a strong league; and men be better and more surely knit together by love and bene-volence, than by covenauntes of leagues; by hartie affection of minde, than by wordes.' With the countries of Europe to-day arming on all sides, and the League of Nations an apparently helpless spectator, one can only breathe a pious wish and hope that the spirit of Utopia might permeate the world.

How then do the views and practices of the Utopians fit in with Catholicism to-day? In many respects, clearly not. Communism involving com-pulsory abolition of private property, does not; dissolution of the marriage tie by divorce, even though confined within narrow limits, does not; euthanasia does not; marriage of the priesthood does not. But as I read the *Utopia*, none of these features in the life of the island of ' Nowhere ' can be said to have the approval of St. Thomas More. He is, as I have said, indicating through the mouth of Hythloday the way in which a non-Christian community without the help of revealed religion would be likely to order its existence, and deal with the various social questions confronting such a community. Nevertheless there is much in the Utopian laws and customs not only consistent with Catholicism, but of its essence. Their condemnation of wars of aggrandisement, their placing the well-being of the people before the enrichment of the ruler, their prevention of the sweating and exploitation of workers by the restriction of hours of labour, the importance of the family as such, their contempt for wealth and outward display, their belief in the immortality of the soul with future rewards for virtue and future punishment for evil, their unpuritanical view that a virtuous life need not be devoid of pleasure ('for they judge it extreme madness to folow sharpe and painful virtue'), their abhorrence of war, all these are views with which the Catholic of to-day finds himself in complete agreement. Moreover, they are views which without doubt commended themselves wholeheartedly to St. Thomas More, who was always on the side of the poor, and of the oppressed, and who viewed men not merely as men, but as has recently been well said—'as personalities, souls, brethren in all their family and religious relations.'

Did St. Thomas More revisit England to-day he would no doubt be able to detect some improvement, some slight approximation to Utopia. Capital punishment has now a very limited application. Labour hours and labour conditions are restricted and supervised. In many other matters improvement is discernible. But nevertheless he would, I fear, have ground for once more admitting 'that many thinges be in the Utopian weale publique which in our cities I maye rather wishe for, than hope after.'

RUSSELL OF KILLOWEN.

CONTENTS

PREFACE

IT used to be confidently asserted that the *Utopia* would be an insuperable bar to St. Thomas More's canonisation. Though Our Holy Father, Pope Pius XI, gave the lie to such assertions by the triumphal ceremony of May 19, 1935, yet More's canonisation as a martyr does not imply approval of all that he said, wrote, or did in his busy life.

The *Utopia* is not the best nor the most important work of Sir Thomas More, yet it is the work by which he is best known, and with which he will always be identified. Not that the book is studied as it deserves—there would be fewer misconceptions of its character if it were—nevertheless its name has passed into use to describe what is visionary, desirable, impracticable, fantastic, daring, or revolutionary. Many earlier writers considered the book as marking our saint's revolt against the mediæval Church, and were able to explain his subsequent martyrdom only by postulating a real or assumed change of opinions.

But the work of Father Bridgett in his *Blessed Thomas More* has not been in vain, and in recent years the writings of Professor Chambers, to whom all lovers of St. Thomas owe so much, have shown the consistency of More's whole life. In many, indeed, of the popular annotated modern editions there is little to complain of, but yet in nearly all, as in Robinson's translation itself, may be found traces of unconscious bias against the Church.

An edition under Catholic auspices is long overdue. Taken in its proper setting and with due understanding of the writer's purpose, the *Utopia* is a work which needs no apology, but is both a striking product of the humanism of the Renaissance and a typically Catholic plea on behalf of Christ's poor.

We have modernised Robinson's text, for our object is not to study English literature, but to assist the general reader to understand More's work, especially in its religious and moral aspect; and after all Robinson is but a translator. For the same reason we have reduced our notes on the historical or classical allusions to a minimum.

It is a pleasure to record here our gratitude for help received from Professor Chambers, R. O'Sullivan, Esq., K.C., and from my colleagues, the Rev. Gordon Albion, D.Hist., F.R.Hist.S., and the Rev. J. J. Curtin, D.D.

PHILIP E. HALLETT.

WONERSH,
July 9, 1937.
Feast of SS. John Fisher and Thomas More.

INTRODUCTION

i. Circumstances of Composition

THE life of St. Thomas More, especially in recent years, has been so often narrated, that we shall content ourselves with a list of the best and most easily accessible accounts (see p. xxxiii) and not attempt to add to the number. The immediate occasion of the writing of the *Utopia* is given by More himself at the beginning of the work and his narrative needs little amplification.

The 'weighty matters of controversy' arose through the breaking off, in 1514, of the proposed marriage between Prince Charles, the future Emperor, and Mary, the sister of Henry VIII. The English king, piqued, forbade the export of wool to Flanders. As there was a most valuable trade in this material, which the Flemish sent back to England manufactured into cloth, Henry found that his short-sighted regulation injured the English as much as the Flemish. He therefore sent an embassy to allay this and other causes of irritation, and for the purpose selected men of such outstanding ability as Tunstall and our saint. It is worth noting how important a place the woollen industry plays in the first book of the *Utopia*.

St. Thomas was one of the most prominent and certainly the most popular of London citizens.

Roper writes that of him ' for his learning, wisdom, knowledge and experience, men had such estimation that . . . at the suit and instance of the English merchants, he was by the king's consent made twice ambassador in certain great causes between them and the merchants of the Stillyard.' These were the merchants of the Hanseatic League, and the Stillyard or Steelyard, the quarter of the City occupied by them, was where Cannon Street Station now stands (Roper, p. 9, and note on p. 110, where it is pointed out that the second embassy to which Roper refers—that of 1517—was not concerned with the Stillyard).

On the title-page of the *Utopia* St. Thomas is described as ' Vicecomes ' of London. He was in fact Under-Sheriff, to which office he had been appointed on September 3, 1510. He was appointed to the embassy on May 7, 1515. On the next day the Court of Aldermen agreed that during his absence ' his sufficient deputy ' should be allowed to ' occupy his room and office until his coming home again ' (Harpsfield, notes, p. 313). He set out on May 12 (L. and P. ii, 678, p. 180), but did not arrive at Bruges until May 7 (Harpsfield, notes, p. 315).

The negotiations dragged out tiresomely. More had hoped they would be over in two months, but they lasted six. It was during the enforced leisure of these tedious days that More wrote Book II of the *Utopia*, by far the longer of the two. The account given at the opening of Book I is true in fact : fiction begins only with Hythloday.

Book I, written to introduce the account given of *Utopia* in Book II, was composed in England in the spring or summer of 1516. It reflects the overtures that were being made to our saint to enter the king's service, overtures all the more pressing because of the success of the Flemish embassy. During the summer Erasmus was staying with More at his house in Bucklersbury, no doubt read what he had written, and urged him to get it printed.[1] It was not finished, however, when Erasmus, towards the end of August, left to return to the Continent, but, on September 3, More was able to send on to him the completed manuscript. The beginning of the letter to Peter Giles, which forms an introduction, seems to show that at the time of his return to England More had promised to write, without delay, the introductory Book I (Giles had presumably read Book II in Flanders upon its composition), but had taken a year to carry out his intention. The letter vividly pictures the difficulties a busy man like St. Thomas found in making time for writing (below p. 11).

ii. THE CHARACTER OF THE *UTOPIA*

In the well-known letter to Ulrich von Hutten[2] Erasmus alludes to the different conditions under which the two books were composed, the second at leisure, the first in the odd moments that could be stolen from a busy life, and sees accordingly some inequality of diction in the two. It is not

[1] A rumour gained currency that Erasmus was the actual writer of the book.

[2] A famous humanist (1488–1523) and author of many works. Unfortunately he joined Luther's revolt and died out of the Church.

difficult to see, in More's Latin style, some of the characteristics of his English writings. In both he displays his ready command of an abundant vocabulary; he chooses words from every quarter (the *Utopia* adopts many words from Plautus), and has no hesitation in himself coining words when convenient. We know that he was a most skilful *ex tempore* speaker both in English and Latin, and when he wrote thoughts and words came to him with equal readiness. He poured out upon paper what was in his mind, making very few corrections in his MSS., and often writing sentences of enormous length. In the first book, for example, the Latin sentence which corresponds with the words ' Here, while one counselleth to conclude a league with the Venetians,' etc., runs to 72 lines, and after a break of a couple of lines is followed by one that runs to 135 lines (Delcourt, pp. 81–90). More will not be fettered. Like the other humanists he desired to write, not a dead, but a living language. They aimed at a renascence, a new bringing to life of Greek and Latin as vehicles of everyday speech. Thus More permits himself an occasional licence of construction, or change of sequence, which, tolerable enough in the spoken word, might be frowned upon by classical purists. Yet his Latin style was much admired by his contemporaries for its vigour and eloquence. We need not suppose that Peter Giles's judgment was warped by affection when he wrote, in his introductory letter to Busleyden, of his admiration for ' the efficacy and pith of his words,' ' so fine a Latin style, with such force of eloquence.'

Among the motives which led St. Thomas to

write the *Utopia* some weight at least must be given to his love of writing for writing's sake, his desire to practise his pen and improve his style. In the letter to von Hutten already quoted Erasmus says of him : 'For a long time he strove to make his prose style more flexible, exercising his pen in every kind of composition. . . . He took especial delight in declamations, and the more paradoxical their argument, the more scope did he consider they offered to the keenness of his wit. He even went so far in his youth as to propose to compose a dialogue in defence of Plato's community of wives.' Stapleton bears similar witness, saying, for example, that he wrote his *Richard III* in Latin 'only to practise his pen' (p. 34).

We must bear in mind, too, that More was an incorrigible joker. His friends nick-named him Democritus, the laughing philosopher, and he 'ragged' even his own family unmercifully. They could not tell when he was serious, for 'he often looked sadly when he meant merrily.' Partly at least, the *Utopia* was a *jeu d'esprit* written for the amusement of his friends. Erasmus urges his correspondents to procure copies if they want a good laugh. His learned friends would enjoy his sallies and take them with the necessary grain of salt. It was written in Latin and not translated into English until many years after his death.

Perhaps we are not meant to take too literally More's statement to Archbishop Warham that Peter Giles got the *Utopia* printed without his knowledge (*insciente me curavit excudendum*, Stapleton, p. 83, or in Latin edition of 1612, p. 237), but certain it is that More did not at first intend to publish it, but was overborne by the persuasion of his friends (see below, pp. 15, 17).

We do not mean to suggest that More had no serious purpose in writing. Some of his phrases are ringing with fierce indignation at the hard lot of the poor and the injustices he saw around him. Much of the book exhibits a passionate sincerity and much of it is a reflection, if not of his serious convictions, at least of his tastes and preferences. On the other hand, it is the height of absurdity to take fiction of this character as the expression in every detail of More's considered opinions. To disentangle what is serious from what is not is a task beyond human power. Sometimes the matter is plain enough and we have tried to give some guidance in our notes, but, in words which are none the less indispensable for having been so repeatedly quoted, Sir James Mackintosh writes: ' The true notion of the *Utopia* is, that it intimates a variety of doctrines, and exhibits a multiplicity of projects, which the writer regards with almost every possible degree of approbation and shade of assent; from the frontiers of serious and entire belief, through gradations of descending plausibility, where the lowest are scarcely more than the exercises of ingenuity, and to which some wild paradoxes are appended, either as a vehicle or as an easy means (if necessary) of disavowing the serious intention of the whole of this Platonic fiction ' (*Life of More*, London, 1844, p. 61).

It must be remarked, too, that in the dialogue, which by its very form indicates a variety of opinions, More himself enters under his own name and that his role is that of a critic of Hythloday's views.

That most of the evils of the world would be eradicated if men were not grasping and avaricious is clear enough, but whether St. Thomas More thought that anything like the communism he so airily sketched could really be a matter of practical politics we must leave the reader to judge. In his last completed work, the *Dialogue of Comfort*, More argues against it, employing the usual familiar arguments : ' But, cousin, men of substance must there be, for else shall you have more beggars, pardie, than there be, and no man left able to relieve another. For this I think in my mind is a very sure conclusion, that if all the money that is in this country, were to-morrow next brought together out of every man's hand, and laid all upon one heap, and then divided out unto every man alike, it would be on the morrow after worse than it was the day before. For I suppose when it were all equally thus divided among all, the best should be left little better then, than almost a beggar is now. And yet he that was a beggar before, all that he shall be the richer for that he should thereby receive, shall not make him much above a beggar still, but many one of the rich men, if their riches stood but in movable substance, shall be safe enough from riches haply for all their life after.

' Men cannot, you wot well, live here in this world, but if that some one man provide a mean of living for some other many. Every man cannot have a ship of his own, nor every man be a merchant without a stock ; and these things, you wot well, must needs be had ; nor every man cannot have a plough by himself. And who might live by the tailor's craft, if no man were able to put a gown to make? Who by the masonry or who could live a carpenter, if no man were able to build neither church, nor house? Who should be makers of any manner cloth, if there lacked men of substance to set sundry sorts a work? Some man that hath but two ducats in his house, were better forbear them both and leave himself not a farthing, but utterly lose all his own, than that some rich man, by whom he is weekly set a work should of his money lose the one half; for then were himself like to lack work. For surely the rich man's substance is the wellspring of the poor man's living. And therefore here would it fare by the poor man, as it fared by the woman in one of Æsop's fables, which had an hen that laid her every day a golden egg; till on a day she thought she would have a great many eggs at once, and therefore she killed her hen, and found but one or twain in her belly, so that for covetise of those few, she lost many ' (pp. 169–170).

With that we may leave it.

iii. The Sources of the *Utopia*

More's debt to Plato is openly acknowledged and is indeed apparent throughout much of the work. Not only the device of an unknown island, like the Atlantis of the Critias, is due to him, not only the general and magnificent notion of justice as the groundwork of the state, not only the conception of civic communal life, but many even of the details of Utopian life are to be paralleled in his writings, especially the Republic. Plato's guardians

are to have no bolts nor bars to their houses, to touch
no gold nor silver, though they may use these
precious metals to hire foreign mercenaries. Plato
insists that death is to be met, not with fear, but
with gladness ; he attacks lawyers, and asserts that
' there is no one who ever acts honestly in the
administration of States ' (Jowett, II, p. 330). The
philosopher, therefore, would be ' unable alone to
resist all their fierce natures, and therefore he
would be of no use to the State or to his friends,
and would have to throw away his life before he
had done any good to himself or others. And he
reflects upon all this, and holds his peace and does
his own business ' (*ibid.*). We may compare the
argument in the first book upon entering the service
of the king.

Moreover Plato, like More, explicitly states the
tentative nature of his sketch, for the ideal can
never be fully realised (*ibid.*, p. 306), and our convictions may be overturned by further knowledge
(p. 212. Literally ' till some one persuade us otherwise '. Cf. below, p. 156 note).

The lectures which More gave when he was only
twenty-three years old on St. Augustine's *De
Civitate Dei* have unfortunately perished. All that
we know of their contents is Stapleton's statement
that he dealt with the work ' not from the theological
point of view, but from the standpoint of history
and philosophy ' (p. 9). Some have thought that the
Utopia may preserve some of the ideas, if not of
the actual passages, of those lost lectures. We do
not think it likely. We certainly cannot conceive
that St. Thomas took to Flanders his MSS. of
fifteen years before, especially as the leisure that he

had there for writing was as unexpected as it was unwelcome, nor do the general conceptions of the two works coincide. The Kingdom of God is essentially a supernatural kingdom, based on God's revelation to man and on the theological virtues of faith, hope, and charity, whereas the *Utopia* is a sketch of what might be achieved (if ' all men were good, which I think will not be yet this good many years ' [below, p. 83]) without any revelation, but with the natural virtues alone, the four cardinal virtues, as St. Ambrose calls them, of prudence, justice, fortitude, and temperance. To a few parallels, however, we have called attention in the notes.

Of St. Thomas Aquinas our saint was, according to Stapleton (p. 38), a diligent student. In some passages of the *Utopia* he may have had in mind the teaching of the Angelic Doctor. Our references, unless otherwise stated, are to the *Summa Theologica*.

So abundantly does More quote Holy Scripture in his controversial and devotional works, that it is clear he knew the text of the Bible well. He admits the excellence of his memory in general in the letter to Giles (below, p. 12). It is not surprising, therefore, to find Biblical allusions, though often clothed, after the fashion of the humanists, in more classical language.

Our saint's friendship for Erasmus was one of the most striking literary romances of the age (see Stapleton, p. 39). Only a few years before (in 1509) that great scholar had written his *Praise of Folly* in More's house and dedicated it to him. We have seen above that he had again been staying with him at the period of More's composition of the first

book of the *Utopia*. Many parallels might be
pointed out between this work and the sentiments
of Erasmus. We may instance especially the hatred
of war and of every form of cruelty. Dr. Lupton
also refers to the soothing powers of music (below,
p. 126), and to many of the proverbs as having their
parallels in Erasmus, the latter in the *Adagia*.

The *Utopia*, too, bears the reflex of its author's
enthusiasm for classical learning, particularly Greek
learning. In its diffusion the humanists thought
they saw the remedy for the great evils of the age.

It will be noted that not only the title of the
book, from οὐ-τόπος, i.e. nowhere, but most of the
proper names are of Greek origin and a kind of
learned joke played upon unscholarly and credulous
readers. The joke is elaborated in the little-known
letter of St. Thomas More to Peter Giles which
we have translated from the French edition of 1517,
and some of its victims are referred to in the first
letter to Giles (p. 14). One of the lessons of the
book is the eager acceptance by the poor Utopians
of the classical knowledge brought to them, in
contrast to the opposition made by so many
Europeans, and the attractive civilisation they had
been able to build up with such slender resources.

References have also been traced by modern
commentators to Cicero's works, especially *De
Finibus* and *De Natura Deorum*, to the *Lycurgus* of
Plutarch, to the *Germania* of Tacitus and other
classical sources.

A potent inspiration of another kind was the
widening of the horizon by the astounding discoveries of the age. It was but thirteen years since
the date traditionally assigned to the discovery of

America by Christopher Columbus, whatever quali-
fications it may be necessary to make to that claim.
Since that time many stories had been brought
home from the New World. That they formed a
topic of conversation in More's circle is evidenced
by the fact that within six months of the first edition
of *Utopia*, John Rastell, More's brother-in-law, set
out on an ambitious, but ill-fated, expedition to the
New Found Lands. The details may be read in
Professor Reed's *Early Tudor Drama* (p. 11).

One book upon the new discoveries has entered
into the very framework of St. Thomas's story.
This is the Four Voyages of Amerigo Vespucci, of
which More writes (below, p. 33) that they 'be
now in print and abroad in every man's hands.'[1]

On his second voyage he came across a people
of whom he relates (according to Dr. Lupton's
translation) : ' The people live according to nature
and may be called Epicureans rather than Stoics.
. . . Property they have none, but all things are
in common. They live without a king, without any
sovereignty, and every one is his own master. . . .
Gold, pearls, jewels, and all other such like things,
which in this Europe of ours we count riches, they
think nothing of ; nay, they utterly despise them '
(compare below, pp. 132 and 141).

On his fourth voyage he came to a place which
is probably to be identified with Cape Frio (near
Rio de Janeiro), where he left a garrison of twenty-
four men, himself returning to Lisbon. It is the
word which both Vespucci and our saint use
for ' garrison,' i.e. *castellum*, which Robinson has

[1] *Quattuor Americi Vesputii Navigationes*, printed as an
appendix to *Cosmographiae Introductio* (St. Dié, 1507).

taken for a proper noun and translated 'Gulike' (below, p. 33). Hythloday then is represented as one of these twenty-four men and as his travels are said to have extended to Ceylon, we have half the world in which to seek for Utopia.

Professor Reed points out, also, that in 1513 there was published a laudatory account of the customs of Abyssinia on the arrival of an embassy from Prester John. That this may have formed the subject of conversation in our saint's household is very likely, for later on in 1533, his son, John More, published a translation of a later report upon the same people (*Early Tudor Drama*, pp. 79–80).

Of the many later sketches of ideal commonwealths it does not fall within our scope to speak.

iv. BIBLIOGRAPHICAL

We have mentioned that St. Thomas sent his MS. to Erasmus on September 3, 1516. Before the end of the year the first edition was out, printed by Theodore (Thierry) Martens of Alost, printer to the University of Louvain, under the care of Peter Giles of Antwerp. This Louvain edition was followed by the Paris edition of 1517 and the Basle editions of March and November, 1518 (with St. Thomas's *Epigrammata*). There is no need to enumerate the many later editions and foreign translations.

The first translation into English was published in London, 1551. It was the work of Ralph Robinson, a Lincolnshire man born in 1521 and afterwards a fellow of Corpus Christi College, Oxford. His letter of dedication to William Cecil, with whom he had been a fellow-pupil at Stamford Grammar School, may lead us to suspect that his sympathies were with the old religion, but that he had not the courage to let them be known. His second edition, the one we have reprinted in modern spelling, is dated 1556, and perhaps it was because the Catholic Queen Mary was on the throne that he omitted his letter to Cecil with its cringing apology for St. Thomas More's errors and obstinacy. There have been numberless other editions. Robinson's style is vigorous and picturesque, but over-exuberant. Constantly he translates one Latin word by two, three, or even more English terms. The titles to Chapters IV, VI, and VII of the second book may be referred to in illustration, for they represent but one single Latin term in every case. Some other examples are given in the notes.

The Anglican Bishop Burnet published another translation in 1684. It is more correct than Robinson's, though not without its own in-accuracies, but it lacks the liveliness of the earlier work which still, therefore, remains the favourite.

Dr. Joseph H. Lupton's (1836–1905) edition, published by the Clarendon Press in 1895, has been of the greatest value to me as to all subsequent editors. Nearly all the references to classical writers which I have included were pointed out by him, and I have been indebted to him in numberless other ways. A useful edition, confessedly a popu-larisation to a large extent of Dr. Lupton's work, was published for J. Churton Collins by the same Press in 1904. To these two works I refer as 'Lupton' and 'Churton Collins.'

I add a list of other works quoted.

Life and Writings of Blessed Thomas More (1st edition, London, 1891), by Rev. T. E. Bridgett, C.SS.R. Cited as 'Bridgett.'

The Life and Death of Sir Thomas More, by Archdeacon Harpsfield, edited by Dr. E. V. Hitchcock for the E.E.T.S., with historical notes by Professor R. W. Chambers (London, 1932). Cited as 'Harpsfield.'

Thomas More, by R. W. Chambers, Quain Professor of English at University College, London (London, 1935). Cited as 'Chambers.'

The Life of Sir Thomas More, by William Roper, edited by Dr. E. V. Hitchcock for the E.E.T.S. (London, 1935). Cited as 'Roper.'

The Life and Illustrious Martyrdom of Sir Thomas More (Part III of 'Tres Thomae,' Douai, 1588), by Thomas Stapleton. English Translation by Philip E. Hallett (London, 1928). Cited as 'Stapleton.'

L'Utopie. Texte Latin édité par Marie Delcourt (Paris, 1936). Cited as 'Delcourt.'

The Dialogues of Plato, translated by B. Jowett, M.A. (Oxford, 1871). To this work belong all the references to Plato unless otherwise stated.

The Workes of Sir Thomas More . . . in the English tongue (London, 1557). Cited as 'E.W.'

A Dialogue of Comfort against Tribulation. A modernised version edited by Philip E. Hallett (London, 1937). Cited as 'Dialogue of Comfort.'

c

TO THE RIGHT HONOURABLE, AND HIS
VERY SINGULAR GOOD MASTER,

MASTER WILLIAM CECIL,[1]
Esquire,

ONE OF THE TWO PRINCIPAL SECRETARIES TO THE KING'S
MOST EXCELLENT MAJESTY,

RALPH ROBINSON WISHETH CONTINUANCE
OF HEALTH, WITH DAILY INCREASE OF
VIRTUE AND HONOUR

UPON a time, when tidings came to the city of
Corinth that King Philip, father to Alexander
surnamed the Great, was coming thitherward with
an army royal to lay siege to the city, the Corinthians
being forthwith stricken with great fear, began
busily and earnestly to look about them, and to fall
to work of all hands, some to scour and trim up
harness, some to carry stones, some to amend and
build higher the walls, some to rampire and fortify
the bulwarks and fortresses, some one thing and
some another, for the defending and strengthening
of the city. The which busy labour and toil of
theirs when Diogenes the philosopher saw, having
no profitable business whereupon to set himself to
work (neither any man required his labour and
help as expedient for the commonwealth in that
necessity), immediately girded about him his

---

[1] In the edition of 1551, but omitted in that of 1556.

philosophical cloak, and began to roll and tumble up and down hither and thither upon the hillside, that lieth adjoining to the city, his great barrel or tun wherein he dwelt; for other dwelling-place would he have none.

This seeing, one of his friends, and not a little musing thereat, came to him: ' And I pray thee, Diogenes ' (quoth he) ' why doest thou thus, or what meanest thou hereby ? ' ' Forsooth I am tumbling my tub too ' (quoth he) ' because it were no reason that I only should be idle where so many be working.'

In semblable manner, right honourable sir, though I be, as I am indeed, of much less ability than Diogenes was to do anything that shall or may be for the advancement and commodity of the public wealth of my native country ; yet I, seeing every sort and kind of people in their vocation and degree busily occupied about the commonwealth's affairs ; and especially learned men daily putting forth in writing new inventions and devices to the furtherance of the same ; thought it my bounded duty to God, and to my country, so to tumble my tub, I mean so to occupy and exercise myself in bestowing such spare hours as I, being at the beck and commandment of others, could conveniently win to myself ; that though no commodity of that my labour and travail to the public weal should arise, yet it might by this appear that mine endeavour and goodwill hereunto was not lacking.

To the accomplishment, therefore, and fulfilling of this my mind and purpose, I took upon me to turn and translate out of Latin into our English tongue the fruitful and profitable book which Sir

Thomas More, knight, compiled and made of the new isle Utopia, containing and setting forth the best state and form of a public weal, a work (as it appeareth) written almost forty years ago by the said Sir Thomas More the author thereof. The which man, forasmuch as he was a man of late time, yea almost of these our days ; and for the excellent qualities wherewith the great goodness of God had plentifully endowed him, and for the high place and room whereunto his prince had most graciously called him, notably well known, not only among us his countrymen, but also in foreign countries and nations ; therefore I have not much to speak of him. This only I say : that it is much to be lamented of all, and not only of us Englishmen, that a man of so incomparable wit, of so profound knowledge, of so absolute learning, and of so fine eloquence, was yet nevertheless so much blinded, rather with obstinacy than with ignorance, that he could not, or rather would not, see the shining light of God's holy truth in certain principal points of Christian religion ; but did rather choose to per-severe and continue in his wilful and stubborn obstinacy even to the very death. This I say is a thing much to be lamented.

But letting this matter pass, I return again to Utopia, which (as I said before) is a work not only for the matter that it containeth, fruitful and profit-able, but also for the writer's eloquent Latin style, pleasant and delectable. Which he that readeth in Latin, as the author himself wrote it, perfectly understanding the same, doubtless he shall take great pleasure and delight both in the sweet eloquence of the writer, and also in the witty

invention and fine conveyance or disposition of the
matter, but most of all in the good and wholesome
lessons which be there in great plenty and
abundance.

But now I fear greatly that in this my simple
translation, through my rudeness and ignorance in
our English tongue, all the grace and pleasure of
the eloquence wherewith the matter in Latin is
finely set forth may seem to be utterly excluded
and lost; and therefore the fruitfulness of the
matter itself much, peradventure, diminished and
appaired. For who knoweth not, which knoweth
anything, that an eloquent style setteth forth and
highly commendeth a mean matter, whereas, on
the other side, rude and unlearned speech defaceth
and disgraceth a very good matter? According
as I heard once a wise man say : A good tale evil
told were better untold, and an evil tale well told
needeth none other solicitor.

This thing I, well pondering and weighing with
myself, and also knowing and knowledging the
barbarous rudeness of my translation, was fully
determined never to have put it forth in print, had
it not been for certain friends of mine, and especially
one, whom above all other I regarded, a man of
sage and discreet wit, and in worldly matters by
long use well experienced, whose name is George
Tadlowe; an honest citizen of London, and in
the same city well accepted and of good reputation ;
at whose request and instance I first took upon my
weak and feeble shoulders the heavy and weighty
burden of this great enterprise.

This man with divers other, but this man chiefly
(for he was able to do more with me than many

other), after that I had once rudely brought the work to an end, ceased not by all means possible continually to assault me, until he had at the last, what by the force of his pithy arguments and strong reasons, and what by his authority, so persuaded me, that he caused me to agree and consent to the imprinting hereof. He, therefore, as the chief persuader, must take upon him the danger which upon this bold and rash enterprise shall ensue. I, as I suppose, am herein clearly acquit and discharged of all blame.

Yet, honourable sir, for the better avoiding of envious and malicious tongues, I (knowing you to be a man, not only profoundly learned, and well affected towards all such as either can or will take pains in the well bestowing of that poor talent which God hath endued them with; but also for your godly disposition and virtuous qualities not unworthily now placed in authority and called to honour) am the bolder humbly to offer and dedicate unto your good mastership this my simple work; partly that under the safe conduct of your protection it may the better be defended from the obloquy of them which can say well by nothing that pleaseth not their fond and corrupt judgments, though it be else both fruitful and godly; and partly that by the means of this homely present I may the better renew and revive (which of late, as you know, I have already begun to do) that old acquaintance that was between you and me in the time of our childhood, being then schoolfellows together; not doubting that you for your native goodness and gentleness will accept in good part this poor gift, as an argument or token that mine old goodwill and hearty affection towards you is not, by reason of long tract of time and separation of our bodies, anything at all quailed and diminished, but rather (I assure you) much augmented and increased.

This, verily, is the chief cause that hath encouraged me to be so bold with your mastership. Else truly this my poor present is of such simple and mean sort, that it is neither able to recompense the least portion of your great gentleness to me, of my part undeserved, both in the time of our old acquaintance and also now lately again bountifully showed; neither yet fit and meet for the very baseness of it to be offered to one so worthy as you be. But Almighty God (who therefore ever be thanked) hath advanced you to such fortune and dignity, that you be of ability to accept thankfully as well a man's good will as his gift. The same God grant you and all yours long and joyfully to continue in all godliness and prosperity.

THE TRANSLATOR TO THE
GENTLE READER[1]

THOU shalt understand, gentle reader, that
though this work of Utopia in English comes
now the second time forth in print, yet was it never
my mind nor intent that it should ever have been
imprinted at all, as who for no such purpose took
upon me at the first the translation thereof; but did
it only at the request of a friend, for his own private
use, upon hope that he would have kept it secret to
himself alone. Whom though I knew to be a man
indeed, both very witty and also skilful, yet was I
certain that in the knowledge of the Latin tongue
he was not so well seen as to be able to judge of the
fineness or coarseness of my translation. Wherefore I went the more slightly through with it, pro-
pounding to myself therein rather to please my said
friend's judgment than mine own. To the meanness
of whose learning I thought it my part to submit
and attemper my style. Lightly, therefore, I over-
ran the whole work, and in short time, with more
haste than good speed, I brought it to an end. But,
as the Latin proverb sayeth: 'The hasty bitch
bringeth forth blind whelps.' For when this my
work was finished, the rudeness thereof showed it to
be done in post-haste.

Howbeit, rude and base though it were, yet

[1] From the edition of 1556.

fortune so ruled the matter that to imprinting it
came, and that partly against my will. Howbeit,
not being able in this behalf to resist the pithy persuasions of my friends, and perceiving therefore
none other remedy, but that forth it should, I
comforted myself for the time only with this notable
saying of Terence—

> *Ita vita est hominum, quasi quum ludas tesseris.*
> *Si illud, quod est maxume opus jactu non cadit :*
> *Illud, quod cecidit forte, id arte ut corrigas.*

In which verses the poet likeneth or compareth the
life of man to a dice-playing or a game at the tables :
meaning therein, if that chance rise not which is
most for the player's advantage, that then the
chance, which fortune hath sent, ought so cunningly
to be played, as may be to the player least damage.
By the which worthy similitude surely the witty
poet giveth us to understand, that though in any of
our acts and doings (as oft chanceth) we happen to
fail and miss of our good pretensed purpose, so
that the success and our intent prove things far
odd ; yet so we ought with witty circumspection to
handle the matter, that no evil or incommodity, as
far forth as may be, and as in us lieth, do thereof
ensue.

According to the which counsel, though I am
indeed in comparison of an expert gamester and
a cunning player but a very bungler, yet have I
in this by chance, that on my side unawares hath
fallen, so (I suppose) behaved myself that, as
doubtless it might have been of me much more
cunningly handled had I forethought so much or
doubted any such sequel at the beginning of my

play, so I am sure it had been much worse than it is if I had not in the end looked somewhat earnestly to my game. For though this work came not from me so fine, so perfect, and so exact yet at first, as surely for my small learning it should have done if I had then meant the publishing thereof in print; yet I trust I have now in this second edition taken about it such pains that very few great faults and notable errors are in it to be found. Now, therefore, most gentle reader, the meanness of this simple translation, and the faults that be therein (as I fear much there be some), I doubt not but thou wilt, in just consideration of the premises, gently and favourably wink at them. So doing thou shalt minister unto me good cause to think my labour and pains herein not altogether bestowed in vain. *Vale!*

THOMAS MORE TO PETER GILES
SENDETH GREETING[1]

I AM almost ashamed, right well-beloved Peter
Giles,[2] to send unto you this book of the
Utopian commonwealth, well-nigh after a year's
space, which I am sure you looked for within a
month and a half. And no marvel. For you knew
well enough that I was already disburdened of all
the labour and study belonging to the invention
in this work, and that I had no need at all to trouble
my brains about the disposition or conveyance of
the matter; and therefore had herein nothing else
to do, but only to rehearse those things which you
and I together heard master Raphael tell and
declare. Wherefore there was no cause why I
should study to set forth the matter with eloquence;
forasmuch as his talk could not be fine and eloquent,
being first not studied for, but sudden and unpre-
meditated, and then, as you know, of a man better

[1] Translated by Robinson from the 1st edition, 1516.
[2] Peter Giles, *Petrus Ægidius*, about eight years younger
than St. Thomas More, was a close friend of Erasmus and
many other contemporary scholars, and himself the author
of many poems. At the time he met More (1516) he was
Town Clerk or Actuary of Antwerp. He acted also as
corrector to Thierry Martens' printing press and arranged
there for the first edition of the *Utopia*. Quentin Metsys'
diptych of Giles and Erasmus, sent as a present to St. Thomas
in September, 1517, is a perpetual memorial of the friendship
of these three scholars. Giles died in 1533.

seen in the Greek language than in the Latin tongue. And my writing, the nearer it should approach to his homely, plain, and simple speech, so much the nigher should it go to the truth : which is the only mark whereunto I do and ought to direct all my travail and study herein.

I grant and confess, friend Peter, myself discharged of so much labour, having all these things ready done to my hand, that almost there was nothing left for me to do. Else either the invention or the disposition of this matter might have required of a wit neither base, neither at all unlearned, both some time and leisure, and also some study. But if it were requisite and necessary that the matter should also have been written eloquently, and not alone truly, of a surety that thing could I have performed by no time nor study. But now seeing all these cares, stays, and lets were taken away, wherein else so much labour and study should have been employed, and that there remained no other thing for me to do but only to write plainly the matter as I heard it spoken ; that indeed was a thing light and easy to be done. Howbeit to the dispatching of this so little business, my other cares and troubles did leave almost less than no leisure. While I do daily bestow my time about law matters ; some to plead, some to hear, some as an arbitrator with mine award to determine, some as an umpire or a judge with my sentence finally to discuss ; while I go one way to see and visit my friend, another way about mine own private affairs ; while I spend almost all the day abroad among others, and the residue at home among mine own ; I leave to myself, I mean to my book, no time.

For when I am come home, I must commune
with my wife, chat with my children, and talk with
my servants. All the which things I reckon and
account among business, forasmuch as they must
of necessity be done : and done must they needs
be, unless a man will be a stranger in his own house.
And in any wise a man must so fashion and order
his conditions, and so appoint and dispose himself,
that he be merry, jocund, and pleasant among them,
whom either nature hath provided, or chance hath
made, or he himself hath chosen to be the fellows
and companions of his life ; so that with too much
gentle behaviour and familiarity he do not mar
them, and by too much sufferance, of his servants
make them his masters.

Among these things now rehearsed, stealeth away
the day, the month, the year. When do I write,
then ? And all this while have I spoken no word of
sleep, neither yet of meat, which among a great
number doth waste no less time than doth sleep,
wherein almost half the lifetime of man creepeth
away. I therefore do win and get only that time
which I steal from sleep[1] and meat. Which time,
because it is very little, and yet somewhat it is,
therefore have I once at the last, though it be long
first, finished Utopia, and have sent it to you, friend
Peter, to read and peruse, to the intent that if anything have escaped me, you might put me in remembrance of it. For though in this behalf I do not
greatly mistrust myself (which would God I were
somewhat in wit and learning, as I am not all of

---

[1] *steal from sleep.* Stapleton (pp. 9 and 31) relates that
More gave but four or five hours each night to sleep, rising
at 2 a.m. for prayer and study.

the worst and dullest memory), yet have I not so great trust and confidence in it that I think nothing could fall out of my mind.

For John Clement,[1] my boy, who as you know was there present with us, whom I suffer to be away from no talk wherein may be any profit or goodness (for out of this young-bladed and new-shot-up corn, which hath already begun to spring up both in Latin and Greek learning, I look for plentiful increase at length of goodly ripe grain), he I say hath brought me into a great doubt. For whereas Hythloday (unless my memory fails me) said that the bridge of Amaurote, which goeth over the river of Anyder, is five hundred paces, that is to say, half a mile in length : my John sayeth that two hundred of those paces must be plucked away, for that the river containeth there not above three hundred paces in breadth. I pray you heartily call the matter to your remembrance. For if you agree with him, I also will say as you say, and confess myself deceived. But if you cannot remember the thing, then surely I will write as I have done, and as mine own remembrance serveth me. For as I will take good heed that there be in my book nothing false, so if there be anything in doubt, I will rather tell a lie than make a lie ;[2] because I had rather be good than wily.

[1] *John Clement.* More took him from Colet's school at St. Paul's to educate him with his family as he himself had been taken into the household of Archbishop Morton at Lambeth. Clement, who, fiction apart, seems really to have accompanied More to Flanders, afterwards became a competent Greek scholar and a Doctor of Medicine. (Stapleton, p. 98.)

[2] *tell a lie than make a lie.* More would prefer to say what he thinks to be true, even though in fact he should be

Howbeit this matter may easily be remedied, if you will take the pains to ask the question of Raphael himself by word of mouth, if he be now with you, or else by your letters. Which you must needs do for another doubt also that hath chanced, through whose fault I cannot tell: whether through mine, or yours, or Raphael's. For neither we remembered to inquire of him, nor he to tell us, in what part of that new world Utopia is situate. The which thing, I had rather have spent no small sum of money, than that it should thus have escaped us; as well for that I am ashamed to be ignorant in what sea that island standeth, whereof I write so long a treatise, as also because there be with us certain men, and especially one virtuous and godly man, and a professor of divinity, who is exceeding desirous to go unto Utopia; not for a vain and curious desire to see news, but to the intent he may further and increase our religion, which is there already luckily begun. And that he may the better accomplish and perform this his good intent, he is minded to procure that he may be sent thither by the high bishop;[1] yea, and that he himself may be made bishop of Utopia, being nothing scrupulous herein, that he must obtain this bishopric with suit. For he counteth that a godly suit which proceedeth not of the desire of honour or lucre, but only of a godly zeal.

mistaken. We may note how More keeps up the fiction on which the whole book is based. 'Many times,' as the Messenger said in More's Dialogue, 'men doubt whether ye speak in sport when ye mean good earnest,' for 'ye use to look so sadly when ye mean merrily.' (E. W., p. 127.)

[1] *the high bishop*. *Pontifice* should be translated 'the Pope,' but Robinson is afraid of the word here as elsewhere.

Wherefore I most earnestly desire you, friend
Peter, to talk with Hythloday, if you can, face to
face, or else to write your letters to him, and so to
work in this matter that in this my book there may
neither anything be found which is untrue, neither
anything be lacking which is true. And I think
verily it shall be well done that you show unto him
the book itself. For if I have missed or failed in
any point, or if any fault have escaped me, no man
can so well correct and amend it as he can; and
yet that can he not do, unless he peruse and read
over my book written. Moreover by this means
shall you perceive whether he be well willing and
content that I should undertake to put this work in
writing. For if he be minded to publish and put
forth his own labours and travels himself, perchance
he would be loath, and so would I also, that in
publishing the Utopian weal public, I should prevent
him, and take from him the flower and grace of the
novelty of this his history.

Howbeit, to say the very truth, I am not yet
fully determined with myself whether I will put
forth my book or no. For the natures of men be
so divers, the fantasies of some so wayward, their
minds so unkind, their judgments so corrupt, that
they which lead a merry and a jocund life, following
their own sensual pleasures and carnal lusts,[1] may
seem to be in a much better state or case than they
that vex and unquiet themselves with cares and
study for the putting forth and publishing of some
thing that may be either profit or pleasure to others ;
which others nevertheless will disdainfully, scorn-

[1] *their own sensual pleasures and carnal lusts.* The Latin
means merely ' following their inclinations.'

D

fully, and unkindly accept the same. The most part of all be unlearned, and a great number hath learning in contempt. The rude and barbarous alloweth nothing but that which is very barbarous indeed. If it be one that hath a little smack of learning, he rejecteth as homely gear and common ware whatsoever is not stuffed full of old moth-eaten terms, and that be worn out of use. Some there be that have pleasure only in old rusty antiquities, and some only in their own doings. One is so sour, so crabbed, and so unpleasant, that he can away with no mirth nor sport. Another is so narrow between the shoulders, that he can bear no jests nor taunts. Some silly poor souls be so afraid that at every snappish word their nose shall be bitten off, that they stand in no less dread of every quick and sharp word than he that is bitten of a mad dog feareth water. Some be so mutable and wavering, that every hour they be in a new mind, saying one thing sitting and another thing standing. Another sort sitteth upon their ale-benches, and there among their cups they give judgment of the wits of writers, and with great authority they condemn even as pleaseth them every writer according to his writing, in most spiteful manner mocking, louting, and flouting them, being themselves in the mean season safe, and as sayeth the proverb, out of all danger of gun-shot. For why, they be so smug and smooth, that they have not so much as one hair of an honest man whereby one may take hold of them. There be, moreover, some so unkind and ungentle, that though they take great pleasure and delectation in the work, yet for all that they cannot find in their hearts to love the author thereof, nor to afford him a good word, being much like uncourteous, un-thankful, and churlish guests, which when they have with good and dainty meats well filled their bellies, depart home, giving no thanks to the feast-maker. Go your ways now, and make a costly feast at your own charges for guests so dainty-mouthed, so diverse in taste, and besides that of so unkind and unthankful natures.

But nevertheless, friend Peter, do, I pray you, with Hythloday as I willed you before. And as for this matter I shall be at my liberty afterwards to take new advisement. Howbeit, seeing I have taken great pains and labour in writing the matter, if it may stand with his mind and pleasure, I will, as touching the edition or publishing of the book, follow the counsel and advice of my friends, and specially yours. Thus fare you well, right heartily beloved friend Peter, with your gentle wife; and love me as you have ever done, for I love you better than ever I did.

TO THE RIGHT HONOURABLE
JEROME BUSLEYDEN,[1]
PROVOST OF AIRE, AND COUNSELLOR TO THE CATHOLIC KING
CHARLES,

PETER GILES, CITIZEN OF ANTWERP,
WISHETH HEALTH AND FELICITY

THOMAS MORE, the singular ornament of
this our age, as you yourself (right honourable
Busleyden) can witness, to whom he is perfectly
well known, sent unto me this other day the island
of Utopia, to very few as yet known, but most
worthy, which as far excelling Plato's commonwealth, all people should be willing to know;
specially of a man most eloquent, so finely set
forth, so cunningly painted out, and so evidently
subject to the eye, that as oft as I read it, methinketh
that I see somewhat more than when I heard
Raphael Hythloday himself (for I was present at
that talk as well as Master More) uttering and
pronouncing his own words: yea, though the same
man, according to his pure eloquence, did so open
and declare the matter, that he might plainly enough
appear to report not things which he had learned of
others only by hearsay, but which he had with his
own eyes presently seen, and thoroughly viewed,
and wherein he had no small time been conversant
and abiding; a man truly, in mine opinion, as

[1] Translated by Robinson from the 1st. edition, 1516.

touching the knowledge of regions, peoples, and worldly experience, much passing, yea, even the very famous and renowned traveller Ulysses; and indeed such a one as for the space of these eight hundred years past I think nature into the world brought not forth his like; in comparison of whom Vespucci may be thought to have seen nothing. Moreover, whereas we be wont more effectually and pithily to declare and express things that we have seen, than which we have but only heard, there was besides that in this man a certain peculiar grace, and singular dexterity to describe and set forth a matter withal.

Yet the selfsame things as oft as I behold and consider them drawn and painted out with Master More's pencil, I am therewith so moved, so delighted, so inflamed, and so rapt, that sometimes methink I am presently conversant even in the island of Utopia. And I promise you, I can scant believe that Raphael himself by all that five years' space that he was in Utopia abiding, saw there so much as here in Master More's description is to be seen and perceived. Which description with so many wonders and miraculous things is replenished, that I stand in great doubt whereat first and chiefly to muse or marvel; whether at the excellency of his perfect and sure memory, which could wellnigh word by word rehearse so many things once only heard; or else at his singular prudence, who so well and wittily marked and bore away all the original causes and fountains (to the vulgar people commonly most unknown) whereof both issueth and springeth the mortal confusion and utter decay of a commonwealth, and also the advancement and wealthy state of the same may rise and grow ; or else at the efficacy and pith of his words, which in so fine a Latin style, with such force of eloquence hath couched together and comprised so many and divers matters, specially being a man continually encumbered with so many busy and troublesome cares, both public and private, as he is.

Howbeit all these things cause you little to marvel (right honourable Busleyden), for that you are familiarly and thoroughly acquainted with the notable, yea almost divine wit of the man.

But now to proceed to other matters, I surely know nothing needful or requisite to be adjoined unto his writings. Only a metre of four verses written in the Utopian tongue, which after Master More's departure Hythloday by chance showed me, that have I caused to be added thereto, with the alphabet of the same nation. For, as touching the situation of the island, that is to say, in what part of the world Utopia standeth, the ignorance and lack whereof not a little troubleth and grieveth Master More, indeed Raphael left not that unspoken of. Howbeit with very few words he lightly touched it, incidentally by the way passing it over, as meaning of likelihood to keep and reserve that to another place. And the same, I wot not how, by a certain evil and unlucky chance escaped us both. For when Raphael was speaking thereof, one of Master More's servants came to him and whispered in his ear. Wherefore, I being then of purpose more earnestly addicted to hear, one of the company, by reason of cold taken, I think, a shipboard, coughed out so loud, that he took from my hearing certain of his words. But I will never

stint, nor rest, until I have got the full and exact
knowledge hereof; insomuch that I will be able
perfectly to instruct you, not only in the longitude
or true meridian of the island, but also in the just
latitude thereof, that is to say, in the sublevation or
height of the pole in that region, if our friend
Hythloday be in safety, and alive.

For we hear very uncertain news of him. Some
report that he died in his journey homeward.
Some again affirm that he returned into his country,
but partly for that he could not away with the
fashions of his country folk, and partly for that his
mind and affection was altogether set and fixed
upon Utopia, they say that he hath taken his voyage
thitherward again.

Now as touching this, that the name of this island
is nowhere found among the old and ancient
cosmographers, this doubt Hythloday himself very
well dissolved. 'For why it is possible enough,'
(quoth he) ' that the name, which it had in old
time, was afterward changed, or else that they
never had knowledge of this island : forasmuch
as now in our time divers lands be found, which
to the old geographers were unknown.' Howbeit,
what needeth it in this behalf to fortify the matter
with arguments, seeing Master More is author
hereof sufficient ?

But whereas he doubteth of the edition or
imprinting of the book, indeed herein I both
commend, and also acknowledge the man's modesty.
Howbeit unto me it seemeth a work most unworthy
to be long suppressed, and most worthy to go
abroad into the hands of men, yea, and under the
title of your name to be published to the world ;

either because the singular endowments and qualities of Master More be to no man better known than to you, or else because no man is more fit and meet than you with good counsels to further and advance the commonwealth, wherein you have many years already continued and travailed with great glory and commendation, both of wisdom and knowledge, and also of integrity and uprightness. Thus, O liberal supporter of good learning, and flower of this our time, I bid you most heartily well to fare. At Antwerp, 1516, the first day of November.

THOMAS MORE SENDS HIS BEST WISHES TO HIS OWN PETER GILES[1]

I HAVE been highly delighted, my dearest Peter, with the criticism, which has come also to your ears, of that very clever man who in regard to my *Utopia* employs the following dilemma. 'If it is supposed to be true, I consider some details to be rather absurd; if fictitious, I should like to know More's real opinion about some of the matters he relates.'

Whoever this man may be, Peter (and I suspect him to be learned and feel sure he is a friend), I am most grateful to him. Indeed I do not know that anyone, since the book was published, has given me such pleasure as he has by his candid criticism. First of all it is gratifying to find that, whether out of friendship to me or out of real interest in the book, he has not wearied of the task of reading it to the very end. Nor has he read it cursorily or hastily, as priests read their breviaries, those, that is to say, who read them at all, but so slowly and carefully that he weighs carefully every point as he proceeds. Then by the very fact that he disagrees with certain points, he makes it sufficiently evident that his agreement with the rest is not rash but considered. Lastly,

[1] Now first translated from the Latin of the Paris edition of 1517.

by the very terms which he employs to blame me,
he confers on me, indirectly, much more praise
than have those who have tried to flatter me.
For a man who, on reading something faulty that
I may have written, complains that he has been
disappointed, clearly shows what a high opinion
he has conceived of me. As for myself, on the
other hand, if out of all that I have written some
few details at least should not be entirely absurd,
it is much more than I ventured to hope for.

But (for I want, in my turn, to be equally open
with him) I do not see why he should pride himself
on being so sharp-sighted (or, as the Greeks call it,
ὀξυδερχὴς) as to find some of the Utopian customs
rather absurd, or to consider that I have unwisely
contrived certain features in my commonwealth, as
if nowhere else in the world were there any
absurdity, or as if out of all the philosophers no
one, in laying down regulations for the State,
the ruler, or the private house, had ever suggested
anything that could be improved upon. As to
which, if I were not restrained by the reverence I
bear to the memory, consecrated by age, of great
men, I could from any one of them extract propositions which everyone would surely agree with me
in condemning.

But now as he doubts whether *Utopia* is real or
imaginary, I in turn demand his real opinion. I
do not indeed deny that if I had determined to
write about a commonwealth, and the idea of
one had formed itself in my mind, I would not
perhaps have thought it a sin to add fictitious
details so that the truth, thus coated with honey,
might be more palatable to my readers. But in

that case even if I had wished to abuse the ignorance of the unlearned, I should certainly not have omitted to insert indications by which scholars would easily have been able to see through my design. If I had done nothing else I should at least have given such names to the prince, the river, the city, the island, as would have warned the skilful reader that the island exists nowhere, that the city is of shadows, the river without water, and the prince without people. It would not have been difficult to do and would have been much more witty. Unless truth had compelled me, I should certainly not have been so stupid as to use those outlandish, meaningless names, Utopia, Anyder, Amaurote, Ademus.

But, dear Giles, some men are so cautious. Whereas we, in simple faith, wrote out all that Hythloday narrated, they are so wary, so hard to satisfy, that they can scarcely be persuaded to believe it. At any rate, whatever they may think of the story, I am glad to think that they cannot call into question my own veracity, for I can say of my offspring what Mysis in Terence[1] says to prove that the son of Glycery was not supposititious, ' Thank God there were reputable witnesses present at the birth.' For it has, indeed, turned out most fortunately for me that Raphael not only said what he did to you and to me, but to many other men of dignity and credit he said at least as much if not indeed more. Or if they are so unbelieving as not to trust even these, let them go to Hythloday himself, for he is yet living. Only recently I heard from some who had just come

---

[1] *Andria*, iv, 5, 30.

from Portugal that on March 1 last he was as well and strong as ever. Let them ask him, let them worm out the truth from him, if they please, by their questions, but let them understand that all I can do is to reproduce the story faithfully, not to guarantee the truth of what I was told.

Farewell, my dearest Peter, with your delightful wife and clever daughter, to whom my wife sends her best wishes.

THE FIRST BOOK

OF THE COMMUNICATION OF RAPHAEL HYTHLODAY, CONCERNING THE BEST STATE OF A COMMONWEALTH

CONCERNING THE BEST STATE OF A COMMONWEALTH

THE most victorious and triumphant King of England, Henry, the Eighth of that name, in all royal virtues a Prince most peerless, had of late in controversy with Charles,[1] the right high and mighty King of Castile, weighty matters and of great importance. For the debatement and final determination whereof, the King's Majesty sent me ambassador into Flanders, joined in Commission with Cuthbert Tunstall,[2] a man doubtless out of comparison, and whom the King's Majesty of late, to the great rejoicing of all men, did prefer to the office of Master of the Rolls.

But of this man's praises I will say nothing, not because I do fear that small credence shall be given to the testimony that cometh out of a friend's mouth; but because his virtue and learning be greater, and of more excellency, than that I am able to praise them, and also in all places so famous and so perfectly well known, that they need not, nor ought not of me to be praised, unless I would

[1] *Charles.* See Introduction, p. xix.
[2] *Cuthbert Tunstall.* One of More's greatest friends, bishop at one time of London, later of Durham. Although under Henry VIII he accepted the Royal Supremacy, he repented of his weakness and, under Elizabeth, standing firm was deprived and died in confinement. See Stapleton, pp. 48–51.

seem to show and set forth the brightness of the sun with a candle, as the proverb sayeth.

There met us at Bruges (for thus it was before agreed) they whom their Prince had for that matter appointed Commissioners, excellent men all. The chief and the head of them was the Margrave (as they call him) of Bruges, a right honourable man ; but the wisest and the best spoken of them was George Temsice, provost of Cassel,[1] a man, not only by learning, but also by nature, of singular eloquence, and in the laws profoundly learned ; but in reasoning and debating of matters, what by his natural wit, and what by daily exercise, surely he had few fellows. After that we had once or twice met, and upon certain points or articles could not fully and thoroughly agree, they for a certain space took their leave of us, and departed to Brussels, there to know their Prince's pleasure. I in the meantime (for so my business lay) went straight thence to Antwerp.

Whilst I was there abiding, oftentimes among others, but which to me was more welcome than any other, did visit me one Peter Giles, a citizen of Antwerp, a man there in his country of honest reputation, and also preferred to high promotions, worthy truly of the highest. For it is hard to say whether the young man[2] be in learning or in honesty more excellent. For he is both of wonderful

---

[1] *Cassel.* A few miles N. of Hazebrouck (Départ. du Nord).

[2] *young man.* He would now be about twenty-nine. But More, who at the time he wrote the *Utopia* was 37–8, was still spoken of as a young man (*juvenis*). Cf. Stapleton, pp. 31–2.

virtuous conditions, and also singularly well learned, and towards all sorts of people exceeding gentle, but towards his friends so kind-hearted, so loving, so faithful, so trusty, and of so earnest affection, that it were very hard in any place to find a man that with him in all points of friendship may be compared. No man can be more lowly or courteous. No man useth less simulation or dissimulation ; in no man is more prudent simplicity. Besides this, he is in his talk and communication so merry and pleasant, yea and that without harm, that through his gentle entertainment, and his sweet and delectable communication, in me was greatly abated and diminished the fervent desire that I had to see my native country, my wife and my children, whom then I did much long and covet to see, because that at that time I had been more than four months from them.

Upon a certain day when I had heard the divine service[1] in Our Lady's Church,[2] which is the fairest, the most gorgeous and curious church of building in all the City, and also most frequented of people, and the service being done,[3] was ready to go home to my lodging, I chanced to espy this foresaid Peter talking with a certain stranger, a man well stricken

[1] *hearing the divine service.* The Latin (*cum rei divinae inter-fuissem*) means ' When I had assisted at Mass.'

[2] *Our Lady's Church.* The famous Cathedral Church of Antwerp, like so many Cathedral Churches throughout Christendom, is dedicated to Our Lady. One of the canons was brother to Peter Giles.

[3] *the service being done.* Robinson's fear of being suspected of Popery again shows itself. (See his preface.) The words *peracto sacro* are simply a variant of the preceding ones, ' when Mass was over.'

in age, with a black, sunburnt face, a long beard, and a cloak cast homely about his shoulders, whom, by his favour and apparel, forthwith I judged to be a mariner. But the said Peter seeing me, came unto me and saluted me. And as I was about to answer him : ' See you this man ? ' sayeth he (and therewith he pointed to the man that I saw him talking with before). 'I was minded,' quoth he, ' to bring him straight home to you.'

' He should have been very welcome to me,' said I, ' for your sake.'

' Nay ' (quoth he), ' for his own sake, if you knew him ; for there is no man this day living that can tell you of so many strange and unknown peoples and countries as this man can. And I know well that you be very desirous to hear of such news.'

' Then I conjectured not far amiss ' (quoth I), ' for even at the first sight I judged him to be a mariner.'

' Nay' (quoth he),' there ye were greatly deceived : he hath sailed, indeed, not as the mariner Palinurus,[1] but as the expert and prudent prince Ulysses : yea, rather as the ancient and sage philosopher Plato. For this same Raphael Hythloday[2] (for this is his name) is very well learned in the Latin tongue ; but profound and excellent in the Greek language. Wherein he ever bestowed more study than in the

---

[1] *Palinurus*. The pilot of Æneas who allowed slumber to overcome him and fell into the sea, thus never finishing his journey. Ulysses, however, and Plato were keen observers, visited many cities and learned much wisdom in their travels

[2] *Hythloday*. From ὔθλος, trifles, and δαίειν, to distribute (Dr. Lupton), or δάϊος, skilled (Churton Collins).

Latin, because he had given himself wholly to the study of Philosophy. Whereof he knew that there is nothing extant in Latin that is to any purpose, saving a few of Seneca's and Cicero's doings. His patrimony that he was born unto, he left to his brethren (for he is a Portugal born), and for the desire that he had to see and know the far countries of the world, he joined himself in company with Amerigo Vespucci,[1] and in the three last voyages of those four that be now in print and abroad in every man's hands, he continued still in his company, saving that in the last voyage he came not home again with him. For he made such means and shift, what by intreatance, and what by importune suit, that he got licence of Master Amerigo (though it were sore against his will) to be one of the twenty-four which in the end of the last voyage were left in the country of Gulike.[2] He was therefore left behind for his mind's sake,[3] as one that took more thought and care for travelling than dying : having customably in his mouth these sayings :[4] he that hath no grave, is covered with

[1] *Vespucci.* See Introduction, p. xxx.

[2] *Gulike.* The Latin *castello* being printed with a capital was taken by Robinson to be the Latin for Jülich—a town W. of Cologne, by Burnet for New Castile, but it means simply a camp or garrison. (See Introduction, p. xxx). Robinson's error leads him later on to speak of the Gulikianes.

[3] *for his mind's sake.* According to his desire.

[4] *sayings.* The first line is from Lucan, *Pharsaliae*, vii, 819, the second an adaptation of a saying of Anaxagoras, quoted by Cicero in *Quaestiones Tusculanae*, i, § 104 (Dr. Lupton). When later on More's wife upbraided him for choosing to be a prisoner in the Tower rather than do the king's will, he said to her : ' Is not this house as nigh heaven as my own ? ' (Roper, p. 83.)

the sky : and, the way to heaven out of all places
is of like length and distance. Which fantasy of his
(if God had not been his better friend) he had
surely bought full dear.

'But after the departing of Master Vespucci,
when he had travelled through and about many
countries with five of his companions, Gulikianes,
at the last by marvellous chance he arrived in
Taprobane,[1] from whence he went to Calicut,
where he chanced to find certain of his country's
ships, wherein he returned again into his country,
nothing less than looked for.'

All this when Peter had told me, I thanked him
for his gentle kindness, that he had vouchsafed to
bring me to the speech of that man, whose communication he thought should be to me pleasant
and acceptable. And therewith I turned me to
Raphael. And when we had hailed each other, and
had spoken these common words that be customably
spoken at the first meeting and acquaintance of
strangers, we went thence to my house, and there
in my garden, upon a bench covered with green
turf, we sat down talking together.

There he told us how that, after the departing
of Vespucci, he and his fellows that tarried behind
in Gulike began by little and little, through fair and
gentle speech, to win the love and favour of the
people of that country, insomuch that within short
space they did dwell amongst them, not only
harmless, but also occupying with them very
familiarly. He told us also that they were in high
reputation and favour with a certain great man
(whose name and country is now quite out of my

[1] *Taprobane.* The Greek word for Ceylon.

remembrance), which of his mere liberality did bear the costs and charges of him and his five companions, and besides that gave them a trusty guide to conduct them in their journey (which by water was in boats, and by land in wagons) and to bring them to other Princes with very friendly commendations. Thus after many days' journeys, he said, they found towns, and cities, and weal publics, full of people, governed by good and wholesome laws.

For under the line equinoctial,[1] and on both sides of the same, as far as the sun doth extend his course, lieth (quoth he) great and wide deserts and wildernesses, parched, burned, and dried up with continual and intolerable heat. All things be hideous, terrible, loathsome, and unpleasant to behold ; all things out of fashion and comeliness, inhabited with wild beasts and serpents, or, at the leastwise, with people that be no less savage, wild, and noisome than the very beasts themselves be. But a little farther beyond that, all things begin by little and little to wax pleasant ; the air soft, temperate, and gentle ; the ground covered with green grass ; less wildness in the beasts. At the last shall ye come again to people, cities, and towns wherein is continual intercourse and occupying of merchandise and chaffer, not only among themselves and with their borderers, but also with merchants of far countries, both by land and water.

' There I had occasion ' (said he) ' to go to many countries on every side. For there was no ship ready to any voyage or journey, but I and my fellows were into it very gladly received.'

[1] *line equinoctial*. The Equator.

The ships that they found first were made plain, flat and broad in the bottom, troughwise. The sails were made of great rushes, or of wickers, and in some places of leather. Afterward they found ships with ridged keels, and sails of canvas, yea, and shortly after, having all things like ours; the shipmen also very expert and cunning, both in the sea and in the weather. But he said that he found great favour and friendship among them for teaching them the feat and the use of the loadstone, which to them before that time was unknown; and therefore they were wont to be very timorous and fearful upon the sea, nor to venture upon it, but only in the summer time. But now they have such a confidence in that stone that they fear not stormy winter; in so doing farther from care than danger. Insomuch that it is greatly to be doubted lest that thing, through their own foolish hardiness, shall turn them to evil and harm, which at the first was supposed should be to them good and commodious.

But what he told us that he saw in every country where he came, it were very long to declare. Neither is it my purpose at this time to make rehearsal thereof. But peradventure in another place[1] I will speak of it, chiefly such things as shall be profitable to be known, as in special be those decrees and ordinances that he marked to be well and wittily provided and enacted among such peoples as do live together in a civil policy and good order. For of such things did we busily inquire and demand of him, and he likewise very willingly told us of the same. But as for monsters, because they be no news, of them we were nothing

[1] *another place*. More had already written Book II.

inquisitive. For nothing is more easy to be found than be barking Scyllas,[1] ravening Celenos, and Lestrygones, devourers of people, and such-like great and incredible monsters. But to find citizens ruled by good and wholesome laws, that is an exceeding rare and hard thing.

But as he marked many fond and foolish laws[2] in those new-found lands, so he rehearsed divers acts and constitutions, whereby these our cities, nations, countries, and kingdoms may take example to amend their faults, enormities, and errors. Whereof in another place (as I said) I will intreat. Now at this time I am determined to rehearse only that he told us of the manners, customs, laws, and ordinances of the Utopians.[3] But first I will repeat our former communication by the occasion, and (as I might say) the drift whereof he was brought into the mention of that weal public.

For, when Raphael had very prudently touched divers things that be amiss, some here and some there, yea, very many on both parts, and again had spoken of such wise laws and prudent decrees as be established and used, both here among us and also there among them, as a man so perfect and expert in the laws and customs of every several country, as though into what place soever he came guestwise, there he had led all his life : then Peter

[1] *Scyllas*, etc. Of these and similar monsters much may be read in the *Odyssey* and the *Æneid*.

[2] *many fond and foolish laws*. A warning, repeated at the end of the Second Book, that the customs and opinions ascribed to the Utopians must not be assumed to have More's own approval.

[3] *Utopians*. The first mention of these seems rather abrupt, but More had already written Book II.

much marvelling at the man, ' Surely, Master Raphael ' (quoth he), ' I wonder greatly why you get you not into some king's court. For I am sure there is no prince living that would not be very glad of you, as a man not only able highly to delight him with your profound learning, and this your knowledge of countries and peoples, but also meet to instruct him with examples, and help him with counsel. And thus doing, you shall bring yourself in a very good case, and also be of ability to help all your friends and kinsfolk.'

' As concerning my friends and kinsfolk ' (quoth he) ' I pass not greatly for them, for I think I have sufficiently done my part towards them already. For these things that other men do not depart from until they be old and sick, yea, which they be then very loath to leave, when they can no longer keep, those very same things did I, being not only lusty and in good health, but also in the flower of my youth, divide among my friends and kinsfolk; which I think with this my liberality ought to hold them contented, and not to require nor to look that, besides this, I should for their sakes give myself in bondage unto kings.'

' Nay, God forbid that ' (quoth Peter). ' It is not my mind that you should be in bondage to kings, but as a retainer to them at your pleasure,[1] which surely I think is the nighest way that you

[1] *at your pleasure*. There is a play upon words here which it is difficult to render in English and consequently Robinson has omitted the next sentence. Peter says : ' I do not mean that you should serve the king (*servias*) but assist him (*inservias*). Hythloday replies that the difference is but a syllable. Peter goes on : ' But by whatever name you call it I think it is the nighest way, etc.'

can devise how to bestow your time fruitfully,
not only for the private commodity of your friends,
and for the general profit of all sorts of people,
but also for the advancement of yourself to a much
wealthier state and condition than you be now in.'

' To a wealthier condition ' (quoth Raphael) ' by
that means that my mind standeth clean against ?
Now I live at liberty after mine own mind and
pleasure, which I think very few of these great
states[1] and peers of realms can say. Yea, and there
be enough of them that sue for great men's friend-
ships : and therefore think it no great hurt if
they have not me, nor three or four such other
as I am.'

' Well, I perceive plainly, friend Raphael ' (quoth
I), ' that you be desirous neither of riches nor of
power. And truly I have in no less reverence and
estimation a man of your mind, than any of them
all that be so high in power and authority. But
you shall do as it becometh you, yea, and according
to this wisdom, to this high and free courage of
yours, if you can find in your heart so to appoint
and dispose yourself, that you may apply your
wit and diligence to the profit of the weal public,
though it be somewhat to your own pain and
hindrance. And this shall you never so well do,
nor with so great profit perform, as if you be of
some great prince's council, and put into his head
(as I doubt not but you will) honest opinions and
virtuous persuasions. For from the prince, as
from a perpetual well-spring, cometh among the
people the flood of all that is good or evil. But in
you is so perfect learning, that without any

---

[1] *states*. Or estates, i.e. dignitaries.

experience, and again so great experience, that
without any learning, you may well be any king's
counsellor.'

'You be twice deceived, Master More' (quoth
he), 'first in me, and again in the thing itself.
For neither is in me the ability that you force
upon me, and if it were never so much, yet in
disquieting mine own quietness I should nothing
further the weal public. For first of all, the most
part of all princes have more delight in warlike
matters and feats of chivalry (the knowledge whereof
I neither have nor desire) than in the good feats of
peace; and employ much more study, how by
right or by wrong to enlarge their dominions,
than how well and peaceably to rule and govern
what they have already. Moreover, they that be
counsellors to kings, every one of them either is of
himself so wise indeed that he needeth not, or else
he thinketh himself so wise that he will not allow,
another man's counsel, saving that they do shamefully and flatteringly give assent to the fond and
foolish sayings of certain great men. Whose
favours, because they be in high authority with
their prince, by assentation and flattery they labour
to obtain. And verily it is naturally given to all
men to esteem their own inventions best. So
both the raven and the ape think their own young
ones fairest.

'Then if a man in such a company, where some
disdain and have despite at other men's inventions,
and some count their own best, if among such
men (I say) a man should bring forth anything that
he hath read done in times past, or that he hath
seen done in other places, there the hearers fare as

though the whole existimation of their wisdom were in jeopardy to be overthrown and that ever after they should be counted for very dizzards,[1] unless they could in other men's inventions pick out matter to reprehend and find fault at. If all other poor helps fail, then this is their extreme refuge. " These things " (say they) " pleased our forefathers and ancestors ; would God we could be so wise as they were " : and as though they had wittily concluded the matter, and with this answer stopped every man's mouth, they sit down again. As who should say, it were a very dangerous matter if a man in any point should be found wiser than his forefathers were. And yet be we content to suffer the best and wittiest of their decrees to lie unexecuted : but if in anything a better order might have been taken than by them was, there we take fast hold, finding therein many faults. Many times have I chanced upon such proud, lewd,[2] overthwart, and wayward judgments, yea, and once in England.'

' I pray you, sir ' (quoth I), ' have you been in our country ? '

' Yea, forsooth ' (quoth he), ' and there I tarried for the space of four or five months together, not long after the insurrection[3] that the western Englishmen made against their king, which by their own miserable and pitiful slaughter was suppressed and ended.

' In the mean season I was much bound and

[1] *dizzards*. Clowns.

[2] *lewd*. Ignorant, from the Anglo-Saxon word, *laewede*, meaning ' lay,' i.e. not a clerk or scholar.

[3] *insurrection*. The Cornish rebellion of 1497.

beholden to the right reverend father, John Morton,[1] Archbishop and Cardinal of Canterbury, and at that time also Lord Chancellor of England; a man, Master Peter (for Master More knoweth already that I will say), not more honourable for his authority than for his prudence and virtue. He was of a mean stature, and though stricken in age, yet bore he his body upright. In his face did shine such an amiable reverence as was pleasant to behold, gentle in communication, yet earnest and sage. He had great delight many times with rough speech to his suitors, to prove, but without harm, what prompt wit and what bold spirit were in every man. In the which, as in a virtue much agreeing with his nature, so that therewith were not joined impudence, he took great delectation. And the same person, as apt and meet to have an administration in the weal public, he did lovingly embrace. In his speech he was fine, eloquent, and pithy. In the law he had profound knowledge, in wit he was incomparable, and in memory wonderful excellent. These qualities, which in him were by nature singular, he by learning and use had made perfect.

' The King put much trust in his counsel, the weal public also in a manner leaned unto him, when I was there. For even in the chief of his youth he was taken from school into the court, and there

[1] *Morton.* It was into his palace at Lambeth that More was taken as page about the year 1490 when he was a boy of about twelve. (See below, p. 69). Morton became archbishop of Canterbury in 1486, Lord Chancellor in 1487, and Cardinal in 1493. More was always loyal to his memory, but others have painted a less favourable picture.

passed all his time in much trouble and business, being continually tumbled and tossed in the waves of divers misfortunes and adversities. And so by many and great dangers he learned the experience of the world, which so being learned cannot easily be forgotten.

'It chanced on a certain day, when I sat at his table, there was also a certain layman cunning in the laws of your realm. Who, I cannot tell whereof taking occasion, began diligently and earnestly to praise that strait and rigorous justice which at that time was there executed upon felons, who, as he said, were for the most part twenty hanged together upon one gallows.[1] And, seeing so few escaped punishment, he said he could not choose but greatly wonder and marvel, how and by what evil luck it should so come to pass, that thieves nevertheless were in every place so rife and so rank.

' " Nay, sir," quoth I (for I durst boldly speak my mind before the Cardinal), " marvel nothing hereat ; for this punishment of thieves passeth the limits of justice, and is also very hurtful to the weal public. For it is too extreme and cruel a punishment for theft, and yet not sufficient to refrain and withhold men from theft. For simple theft is not so great an offence that it ought to be punished with death. Neither there is any punishment so horrible that it can keep them from stealing which have no other craft whereby to get their living. Therefore in this point, not you only, but also the most part of the world, be like evil school-

[1] *gallows.* The original means that felons were to be seen hanging on every side, sometimes as many as twenty upon one gallows.

masters, which be readier to beat, than to teach, their scholars. For great and horrible punishments be appointed for thieves, whereas much rather provision should have been made that there were some means whereby they might get their living, so that no man should be driven to this extreme necessity, first to steal, and then to die."

' " Yes " (quoth he), " this matter is well enough provided for already. There be handicrafts, there is husbandry to get their living by, if they would not willingly be naught."

' " Nay " (quoth I), " you shall not escape so : for first of all, I will speak nothing of them that come home out of the wars maimed and lame, as not long ago out of Blackheath[1] field, and a little before that out of the wars in France : such, I say, as put their lives in jeopardy for the weal public's or the king's sake, and by reason of weakness and lameness be not able to occupy their old crafts, and be too aged to learn new : of them I will speak nothing, forasmuch as wars have their ordinary recourses.[2] But let us consider those things that chance daily before our eyes.

' " First there is a great number of gentlemen which cannot be content to live idle themselves, like drones, off that which others have laboured for : their tenants, I mean, whom they poll and shave to the quick, by raising their rents (for this only point of frugality do they use, men else through their lavish and prodigal spending able to

---

[1] *Blackheath.* Where the Cornish rising above spoken of was finally crushed (June 22, 1497).

[2] *recourses.* The Latin means that wars are occasional and not every-day occurrences.

bring themselves to very beggary), these gentlemen, I say, do not only live in idleness themselves, but also carry about with them at their tails a great flock or train of idle[1] and loitering serving-men, which never learned any craft whereby to get their livings. These men, as soon as their master is dead, or be sick themselves, be incontinent[2] thrust out of doors. For gentlemen had rather keep idle persons than sick men, and many times the dead man's heir is not able to maintain so great a house, and keep so many serving-men as his father did.

' " Then in the mean season, they that be thus destitute of service either starve for hunger, or manfully play the thieves. For what would you have them to do? When they have wandered abroad so long, until they have worn threadbare their apparel, and also impaired their health, then gentlemen, because of their pale and sickly faces and patched coats, will not take them into service. And husbandmen dare not set them awork; knowing well enough that he is nothing meet to do true and faithful service to a poor man with a spade and a mattock for small wages and hard fare, which being daintily and tenderly pampered up in idleness and pleasure, was wont with a sword and a buckler by his side to jet[3] through the street with a bragging look, and to think himself too good to be any man's mate."

' " Nay by St. Mary,[4] sir " (quoth the lawyer), " not so. For this kind of men must we make

---

[1] *idle.* More was careful in his own household to obviate these evils. Cf. Stapleton, Chapter IX.

[2] *incontinent.* Immediately.   [3] *jet.* Strut.

[4] *By St. Mary.* An addition by Robinson.

most of. For in them as men of stouter stomachs, bolder spirits, and manlier courage than handicraftsmen and ploughmen be, doth consist the whole power, strength, and puissance of our army, when we must fight in battle."

' " Forsooth, sir, as well you might say " (quoth I) " that for war's sake you must cherish thieves. For surely you shall never lack thieves, while you have them. No, nor thieves be not the most false and faint-hearted soldiers, nor soldiers be not the cowardliest thieves : so well these two crafts agree together. But this fault, though it be much used among you, yet is it not peculiar to you only, but common also almost to all nations. Yet France besides this is troubled and infected with a much sorer plague. The whole realm is filled and besieged with hired soldiers in peace time (if that be peace) which be brought in under the same colour and pretence that hath persuaded you to keep these idle serving-men. For these wise fools and very archdolts thought the wealth of the whole country herein to consist, if there were ever in a readiness a strong and a sure garrison, specially of old practised soldiers, for they put no trust at all in men unexercised. And therefore they must be forced to seek for war, to the end they may ever have practised soldiers and cunning manslayers, lest that (as it is prettily said of Sallust)[1] their hands and their minds through idleness or lack of exercise should wax dull.

' " But how pernicious and pestilent a thing it is to maintain such beasts, the Frenchmen by their

[1] *Sallust*. The reference is to *De Conjuratione Catilinae*, § XVI.

own harms have learned, and the examples of the
Romans, Carthaginians, Syrians, and of many other
countries do manifestly declare. For not only the
Empire, but also the fields and cities of all these,
by divers occasions have been overrun and destroyed
of their own armies beforehand had in a readiness.
Now how unnecessary a thing this is, hereby it
may appear : that the French soldiers, which from
their youth have been practised and inured in
feats of arms, do not crack nor advance themselves
to have very often got the upper hand and mastery
of your new-made and unpractised soldiers. But
in this point I will not use many words, lest perchance I may seem to flatter you. No, nor those
same handicraftsmen of yours in cities, nor yet
the rude and uplandish ploughmen of the country,
are not supposed to be greatly afraid of your
gentlemen's idle serving-men, unless it be such as
be not of body or stature correspondent to their
strength and courage, or else whose bold stomachs
be discouraged through poverty. Thus you may
see that it is not to be feared lest they should be
effeminated, if they were brought up in good crafts
and laboursome works, whereby to get their
livings, whose stout and sturdy bodies (for gentlemen vouchsafe to corrupt and spill none but picked
and chosen men) now either by reason of rest and
idleness be brought to weakness ; or else by too
easy and womanly exercises be made feeble and
unable to endure hardness. Truly howsoever the
case standeth, this methinketh is nothing available
to the weal public, for war's sake, which you never
have but when you will yourselves, to keep and
maintain an innumerable flock of that sort of men

F

that be so troublesome and noyous[1] in peace,
whereof you ought to have a thousand times more
regard than of war.

' " But yet this is not only the necessary cause of
stealing. There is another, which, as I suppose, is
proper and peculiar to you Englishmen alone."

' " What is that ? " quoth the Cardinal.

' " Forsooth, my lord " (quoth I), " your sheep
that were wont to be so meek and tame, and so
small eaters, now, as I hear say, be become so
great devourers and so wild that they eat up and
swallow down the very men themselves. They
consume, destroy, and devour whole fields, houses,
and cities. For look in what parts of the realm
doth grow the finest, and therefore dearest wool,
there noblemen and gentlemen, yea, and certain
abbots, holy men, no doubt, not contenting
themselves with the yearly revenues and profits
that were wont to grow to their forefathers and
predecessors of their lands, nor being content
that they live in rest and pleasure nothing profiting,
yea much annoying the weal public, leave no ground
for tillage, they enclose all into pastures ; they
throw down houses ; they pluck down towns, and
leave nothing standing, but only the church to be
made a sheephouse. And as though you lost no
small quantity of ground by forests, chases, lands,
and parks, those good holy[2] men turn all dwelling-

---

[1] *noyous.* Harmful.
[2] *holy.* This word is an addition to which nothing
corresponds in the original. We quote Dr. Lupton's
comment. ' The uncalled-for addition of this epithet by
the translator seems intended to point the reproach against
the heads of religious houses, the *abbates aliquot*, who were

places and all glebeland into desolation and wilderness.

' " Therefore that one covetous and unsatiable cormorant and very plague of his native country may compass about and enclose many thousand acres of ground together within one pale or hedge, the husbandmen be thrust out of their own, or else either by covin[1] and fraud, or by violent oppression they be put beside it, or by wrongs and injuries they be so wearied that they be compelled to sell all : by one means, therefore, or by other, either by hook or crook they must needs depart away, poor, silly,[2] wretched souls, men, women, husbands, wives, fatherless children, widows, woeful mothers with their young babes, and their whole household, small in substance and much in number, as husbandry requireth many hands. Away they trudge, I say, out of their known and accustomed houses, finding no place to rest in. All their household stuff, which is very little worth, though it might well abide the sale ;[3] yet being suddenly thrust out, they be constrained to sell it for a thing of naught. And when they have wandered

called *sancti viri* just above. But there is nothing to show that they were more to blame in this respect than other great landlords. It is easy to understand that after the civil wars of the last century their lands might in many cases have become less productive, for want of proper cultivation, and themselves embarrassed with debt ; anxious, therefore, to find some way of making their estates more profitable. See Gasquet's *Henry VIII and the English Monasteries*, 1888, Vol. I, Chap. I.'

[1] *covin*. Fraud.   [2] *silly*. Pitiable.

[3] *abide the sale*, i.e. even if they could choose their own time for selling it.

abroad till that be spent, what can they then else do but steal, and then justly pardy be hanged, or else go about a-begging. And yet then also they be cast in prison as vagabonds, because they go about and work not, whom no man will set a-work, though they never so willingly proffer themselves thereto.[1] For one shepherd or herdman is enough to eat up that ground with cattle, to the occupying whereof about husbandry many hands were requisite. And this is also the cause why victuals be now in many places dearer.

' " Yea, besides this, the price of wool is so risen, that poor folks, which were wont to work it, and make cloth thereof, be now able to buy none at all. And by this means very many be forced to forsake work, and to give themselves to idleness. For after that so much ground was enclosed for pasture, an infinite multitude of sheep died of the rot, such vengeance God took of their inordinate and unsociable covetousness, sending among the sheep that pestiferous murrain, which much more justly should have fallen on the sheepmasters' own heads.

' " And though the number of sheep increase ever so fast, yet the price falleth not one mite, because there be so few sellers.[2] For they be

---

[1] *themselves thereto.* After this comes a sentence which Robinson omitted to translate. ' For there is no demand for the agricultural labour to which they have been accustomed, where there is no further sowing.'

[2] *because there be so few sellers.* The Latin which Robinson thus renders is much fuller. It can be translated : ' And though we cannot speak of a monopoly, for there is not one seller only, yet we might coin the word " oligopoly," for they be almost all come, etc.'

almost all come into a few rich men's hands, whom
no need forceth to sell before they list, and they
list not before they may sell as dear as they list.
Now the same cause bringeth in like dearth of the
other kinds of cattle, yea, and that so much the
more, because that after farms plucked down, and
husbandry decayed, there is no man that passeth[1]
for the breeding of young store. For these rich
men bring not up the young ones of great cattle
as they do lambs. But first they buy them abroad[2]
very cheap, and afterwards when they be fatted
in their pastures, they sell them again exceeding
dear. And therefore (as I suppose) the whole
incommodity hereof is not yet felt. For yet they
make dearth[3] only in those places where they sell.
But when they shall fetch them away from thence
where they be bred faster than they can be brought
up, then shall there also be felt great dearth, store
beginning there to fail where the ware is bought.

' " Thus the unreasonable covetousness of a few
hath turned that thing to the utter undoing of
your island, in the which thing the chief felicity
of your realm did consist. For this great dearth
of victuals causeth men to keep as little houses, and
as small hospitality as they possibly may, and to
put away their servants : whether, I pray you,
but a-begging, or else (which the gentle bloods and
stout stomachs will sooner set their minds unto)
a-stealing ?

' " Now to amend the matter, to this wretched

---

[1] *passeth*. Taketh care.

[2] *abroad*, i.e. in other places. More does not mean overseas.

[3] *make dearth*. The Latin means ' Raise the price.'

beggary and miserable poverty is joined great wantonness, importunate superfluity, and excessive riot. For not only gentlemen's servants, but also handicraftsmen, yea, and almost the ploughmen of the country, with all other sorts of people, use much strange and proud newfangledness in their apparel, and too much prodigal riot and sumptuous fare at their table. Now bawds, queans, whores, harlots, strumpets, brothel-houses, stews, and yet another stews, wine-taverns, ale-houses, and tippling-houses, with so many naughty, lewd, and unlawful games, as dice, cards,[1] tables, tennis, bowls, quoits, do not all these send the haunters of them straight a-stealing when their money is gone?

' " Cast out these pernicious abominations, make a law that they which plucked down farms and towns of husbandry shall re-edify them, or else yield and uprender the possession thereof to such as will go to the cost of building them anew. Suffer not these rich men to buy up all, to engross, and forestall, and with their monopoly to keep the market alone as pleases them. Let not so many be brought up in idleness, let husbandry and tillage be restored, let cloth-working be renewed, that there may be honest labours for this idle sort to pass their time in profitably, which hitherto either poverty hath caused to be thieves, or else now be either vagabonds or idle serving-men, and shortly will be thieves. Doubtless unless you find a remedy for these enormities, you shall in vain advance yourself of executing justice upon felons. For this justice is more beautiful in appearance,

---

[1] *dice, cards.* These are especially mentioned by Stapleton (*l.c.*) as forbidden in More's household.

and more flourishing to the show, than either just
or profitable. For by suffering your youth wantonly
and viciously to be brought up, and to be infected,
even from their tender age, by little and little with
vice, then a God's name to be punished when they
commit the same faults after being come to man's
state, which from their youth they were ever like
to do ; in this point, I pray you, what other thing
do you, than make thieves, and then punish
them ? "

'Now as I was thus speaking the lawyer began
to make himself ready to answer,[1] and was determined with himself to use the common fashion and
trade of disputers, which be more diligent in
rehearsing than answering, as thinking the memory
worthy of the chief praise. "Indeed, sir" (quoth
he), "you have said well, being but a stranger,
and one that might rather hear something of these
matters than have any exact or perfect knowledge
of the same, as I will incontinent by open proffer
make manifest and plain. For, first I will rehearse
in order all that you have said ; then I will declare
wherein you be deceived, through lack of knowledge, in all our fashions, manners, and customs ;

[1] *to answer.* ' To speak ' would be a more exact translation
and more consistent with the remainder of the sentence.
In scholastic disputations it was, and is, the custom to repeat
the argument of the opponent before replying to it. More
satirizes the abuse of such proceedings, but not the disputations themselves. He had his own daughters so highly
trained that they conducted a disputation in philosophy
before the king, probably in 1529. This would have been
in Latin and in scholastic form. See too Stapleton, p. 99.
In the letter to von Hutten, Erasmus tells of More's practice
of taking a personal part in such exercises.

and last of all I will answer your arguments, and confute them every one. First, therefore, I will begin where I promised. Four things you seemed to me."

' " Hold your peace," quoth the Cardinal, " for it appeareth that you will make no short answer, which make such a beginning. Wherefore at this time you shall not take the pains to make your answer, but keep it to your next meeting, which I would be right glad that it might be even to-morrow next, unless either you or Master Raphael have any earnest let.[1]

' " But now, Master Raphael, I would very gladly hear of you, why you think theft not worthy to be punished with death, or what other punishment you can devise more expedient to the weal public. For I am sure you are not of that mind, that you would have theft escape unpunished. For if now the extreme punishment of death cannot cause them to leave stealing, then if ruffians and robbers should be sure of their lives, what violence, what fear were able to hold their hands from robbing, which would take the mitigation of the punishment as a very provocation to the mischief ? "

' " Surely, my lord " (quoth I), " I think it not right nor justice, that the loss of money should cause the loss of man's life. For mine opinion is, that all the goods in the world are not able to countervail man's life. But if they would thus say : that the breaking of justice, and the transgression of the laws is recompensed with this punishment, and not the loss of the money, then why may not this extreme and rigorous justice

[1] *earnest let*. Grave hindrance.

well be called plain injury ? For so cruel governance, so strait rules,[1] and unmerciful laws be not
allowable, that if a small offence be committed,
by and by the sword should be drawn ; nor so
stoical ordinances[2] are to be borne withal, as to
count all offences of such equality, that the killing
of a man, or the taking of his money from him
were both a matter, and the one no more heinous
offence than the other ; between the which two,
if we have any respect to equity, no similitude or
equality consisteth.[3] God commandeth us that we
shall not kill. And be we then so hasty to kill a
man for taking a little money ? And if any man
would understand killing by this commandment of
God to be forbidden after no larger wise than man's

[1] *strait rules*. In the Latin it is *Manliana imperia*, i.e.
decrees as strict as those of Manlius (cf. *Livy*, iv, 29).

[2] *stoical ordinances*. More will have found this view of
the Stoics refuted by St. Thomas Aquinas (Ia–IIae, Q. lxxiii,
a. 2).

[3] *equality consisteth*. ' This paragraph is of considerable
legal interest. The want of proportion between the taking
of money and the loss of life by way of punishment has been
corrected by the law reforms of the nineteenth century. No
man is now sentenced to death for theft. The reference to
equity and equality is also interesting. It was a maxim of the
Chancellor's Office that " equality is equity " and this, of
course, is the teaching of St. Thomas Aquinas in matters
of commutative justice. This passage shows that as early
as 1516–17, long before he was Chancellor, and even before
he entered the regular service of the King, More was
conscious of the defects of the law and of the legal system
and of the necessity of having it corrected by the administration of equity which, in later years as Lord Chancellor, it
was his duty to enforce.'

I owe this note to Mr. Richard O'Sullivan and add to it a
reference to More's own practice as related by Roper (pp. 44,
45).

constitutions define killing to be lawful, then why
may it not likewise by man's constitutions be
determined after what sort whoredom, fornication,
and perjury may be lawful ? For whereas, by the
permission of God, no man neither hath power to
kill neither himself nor yet any other man : then
if a law made by the consent of men, concerning
slaughter of men, ought to be of such strength,
force, and virtue, that they which contrary to
the commandment of God have killed those whom
this constitution of man commanded to be killed,
be clean quite and exempt out of the bonds and
danger of God's commandment ; shall it not then
by this reason follow, that the power of God's
commandment shall extend no further than man's
law doth define and permit ? And so shall it come
to pass that in like manner man's constitutions in
all things shall determine how far the observation
of all God's commandments shall extend. To be
short, Moses' law,[1] though it were ungentle and
sharp, as a law that was given to bondmen, yea,
and them very obstinate, stubborn, and stiff-necked,
yet it punished theft by the purse, and not with
death. And let us not think that God in the new
law of clemency and mercy, under the which He
ruleth us with fatherly gentleness as His dear
children, hath given us greater scope and licence
to the execution of cruelty, one upon another.

[1] *Moses' law. See Exodus*, Chapter XXII. Hythloday's
argument as it stands might be urged not only against the
death penalty for stealing, but against all capital punishment.
Probably More did not intend it to be so taken. At any
rate he himself approved of the death penalty, e.g. in certain
cases of heresy (E. W., pp. 925-6), and ascribed its use to
the Utopians (see below, e.g. pp. 60, 170.)

' " Now ye have heard the reasons whereby I am persuaded that this punishment is unlawful. Furthermore, I think there is nobody that knoweth not how unreasonable, yea, how pernicious a thing it is to the weal public, that a thief and a homicide or murderer, should suffer equal and like punishment. For the thief seeing that man that is condemned for theft in no less jeopardy, nor judged to no less punishment, than him that is convicted of manslaughter, through this cogitation only he is strongly and forcibly provoked, and in a manner constrained, to kill him whom else he would have but robbed. For the murder being once done, he is in less fear, and in more hope that the deed shall not be bewrayed or known, seeing the party is now dead and rid out of the way, which only might have uttered and disclosed it. But if he chance to be taken and descried : yet he is in no more danger and jeopardy than if he had committed but single felony. Therefore whiles we go about with such cruelty to make thieves afraid, we provoke them to kill good men.

' " Now as touching this question, what punishment were more commodious and better ; that truly in my judgment is easier to be found, than what punishment might be worse. For why should we doubt that to be a good and a profitable way for the punishment of offenders, which we know did in times past so long please the Romans, men in the administration of a weal public most expert, politic, and cunning? Such as among them were conceived of great and heinous trespasses, them they condemned into stone quarries, and into mines to dig metal, there to be kept in chains all the days of their life.

' " But as concerning this matter, I allow the
ordinance of no nation so well as that which I
saw, while I travelled abroad about the world,
used in Persia among the people that commonly
be called the Polylerites.[1]   Whose land is both
large and ample, and also well and wittily governed ;
and the people in all conditions free and ruled by
their own laws, saving that they pay a yearly tribute
to the great King of Persia.   But because they be
far from the sea, compassed and enclosed almost
round about with high mountains, and do content
themselves with the fruits of their own land, which
is of itself very fertile and fruitful : for this cause
neither they go to other countries, nor other come
to them.   And according to the old custom of the
land, they desire not to enlarge the bounds of their
dominions ; and those that they have, by reason
of the high hills, be easily defended ; and the tribute
which they pay to their chief lord and king setteth
them quit and free from warfare.   Thus their life is
commodious rather than gallant, and may better
be called happy or wealthy, than notable or famous.
For they be not known as much as by name, I
suppose, saving only to their next neighbours and
borderers.

' " They that in this land be attainted and convict
of felony, make restitution of that which they stole,
to the right owner, and not (as they do in other
lands) to the king ; whom they think to have no
more right to the thief-stolen thing than the thief
himself hath.   But if the thing be lost or made

---

[1] *Polylerites.*   The non-existence of such a people would
be conveyed to the Greek scholar by the name, evidently
derived from πολὺς, much, λῆρος, nonsense.

away, then the value of it is paid of the goods of
such offenders, which else remaineth all whole to
their wives and children. And they themselves be
condemned to be common labourers, and, unless
the theft be very heinous, they be neither locked in
prison, nor fettered in gyves, but be untied and go
at large, labouring in the common works. They
that refuse labour, or go slowly and slackly to
their work, be not only tied in chains, but also[1]
pricked forward with stripes. But being diligent
about their work they live without check or rebuke.
Every night they be called in by name, and be
locked in their chambers. Beside their daily labour,
their life is nothing hard or incommodious. Their
fare is indifferent good, borne at the charges of the
weal public, because they be common servants to
the commonwealth.

' " But their charges in all places of the land is
not borne alike. For in some parts that which is
bestowed upon them is gathered of alms. And
though that way be uncertain, yet the people be so
full of mercy and pity, that none is found more
profitable or plentiful. In some places certain
lands[2] be appointed hereunto ; of the revenues
whereof they be maintained. And in some places
every man giveth a certain tribute for the same
use and purpose. Again, in some parts of the land
these serving-men (for so be these damned persons
called) do no common work, but as every private
man needeth labourers, so he cometh into the

---

[1] *only . . . also.* The omission of these two words would
bring the version more into conformity with the original.

[2] *lands.* There is no reference to lands in the original
which speaks simply of public revenues.

market-place, and there hireth some of them for
meat and drink, and a certain limited wages by
the day, somewhat cheaper than he should hire a
freeman. It is also lawful for them to chastise the
sloth of these serving-men with stripes.

' " By this means they never lack work, and
besides the gaining of their meat and drink every
one of them bringeth daily something into the
common treasury. All and every one of them be
apparelled in one colour. Their heads be not polled
or shaven, but rounded a little above the ears. And
the tip of the one ear is cut off. Every one of
them may take meat and drink of their friends, and
also a coat of their own colour; but to receive
money is death,[1] as well to the giver as to the
receiver. And no less jeopardy it is for a freeman
to receive money of a serving-man for any manner
of cause, and likewise for serving-men to touch
weapons.

' " The serving-men of every several shire be
distinct and known from other by their several and
distinct badges, which to cast away is death; as it
is also to be seen out of the precinct of their own
shire, or to talk with a serving-man of another
shire. And it is no less danger to them for to
intend to run away than to do it indeed. Yea, and
to conceal such an enterprise, in a serving-man it
is death, in a freeman servitude. Of the contrary
part, to him that openeth and uttereth such counsels,
be decreed large gifts: to a freeman a great sum
of money, to a serving-man freedom, and to them

---

[1] *death.* The death penalty seems inconsistent with what
has preceded. The wages paid are to be paid in to the
treasury (see six lines above).

both forgiveness and pardon of that they were of counsel in that pretence. So that it can never be so good for them to go forward in their evil purpose, as by repentance to turn back.

' " This is the law and order in this behalf, as I have shown you. Wherein what humanity is used, how far it is from cruelty, and how commodious it is, you do plainly perceive; forasmuch as the end of their wrath and punishment intendeth nothing else but the destruction of vices and saving of men; with so using and ordering them that they cannot choose but be good, and what harm soever they did before, in the residue of their life to make amends for the same.

' " Moreover, it is so little feared that they should turn again to their vicious conditions, that wayfaring men will for their safeguard choose them to their guides before any other, in every shire changing and taking new. For if they would commit robbery, they have nothing about them meet for that purpose. They may touch no weapons: money found about them should betray the robbery. They should be no sooner taken with the manner, but forthwith they should be punished. Neither they can have any hope at all to escape away by flying. For how should a man, that in no part of his apparel is like other men, fly privily and unknown, unless he would run away naked? Howbeit so also flying he should be descried by the rounding of his head, and his ear-mark. But it is a thing to be doubted, that they will lay their heads together and conspire against the weal public. No, no, I warrant you. For the serving-men of one shire alone could never hope to bring to pass such an enterprise without soliciting, enticing, and alluring the serving-men of many other shires to take their parts. Which thing is to them so impossible, that they may not as much as speak or talk together, or salute one another. No, it is not to be thought that they would make their own countrymen and companions of their counsel in such a matter, which they know well should be jeopardy to the counsellor thereof, and great commodity and goodness to the opener and detector of the same. Whereas, on the other part, there is none of them all hopeless or in despair to recover again his former estate of freedom by humble obedience, by patient suffering, and by giving good tokens and likelihood of himself, that he will ever after that live like a true and an honest man. For every year divers of them be restored to their freedom, through the commendation of their patience."

' When I had thus spoken, saying, moreover, that I could see no cause why this order might not be had in England with much more profit than the justice which the lawyer so highly praised : " Nay," quoth the lawyer, " this could never be so established in England but that it must needs bring the weal public into great jeopardy and hazard." And as he was thus saying, he shook his head and made a wry mouth, and so he held his peace. And all that were there present, with one assent agreed to his saying.

' " Well " (quoth the Cardinal) " yet it were hard to judge without a proof, whether this order would do well here or no. But when the sentence of death is given, if then the king should command

ecution to be deferred and spared, and would
ove this order and fashion, taking away the
vileges of all centuries, if then the proof should
clare the thing to be good and profitable, then
were well done that it were established ; else the
ndemned and reprieved persons may as well and
iustly be put to death after this proof, as when
ere first cast. Neither any jeopardy can in
an space grow hereof. Yea, and methinketh
ese vagabonds may very well be ordered
he same fashion, against whom we have
to made so many laws, and so little prevailed."

When the Cardinal had thus said, then every
man gave great praise to my sayings, which a little
before they had disallowed. But most of all was
esteemed that which was spoken of vagabonds,
because it was the Cardinal's own addition.

' I cannot tell whether[1] it were best to rehearse

---

[1] *I cannot tell whether*, etc. This sentence and the one
following, together with the long anecdote which they
introduce, i.e. ' But a certain friar, graduate, etc. . . . and so
dismissed us,' are omitted in the Louvain edition of More's
Latin Works, 1565, and in some other editions. The
Louvain edition bears an attestation signed by a professor of
theology, ' F. Johannes Hentenius,' to the following effect :
' I consider that these works of Thomas More, *now corrected*,
may be usefully printed and published, for they foster piety
and give a pleasure which is without offence.' More sometimes made fun of monks or friars, chiefly for their resistance
to the spread of classical learning, sometimes he attacked
them on account of abuses, yet Fr. Bridgett is able to write
(p. 87), ' I have been unable to find in the writings of More
any pages that I could wish unwritten or burnt for fear of
scandal to the weak or simple.' More reverenced the
Carthusians and the Brigettines and stayed in their guest-
houses, though when it was a question of his own vocation

G

the communication that followed, for it was n
very sad. But yet you shall hear it, for there w
no evil in it, and partly it pertained to the matt
beforesaid.

'There chanced to stand by a certain jesti
parasite, or scoffer, which would seem to resem'
and counterfeit the fool. But he did in such ·
counterfeit, that he was almost the very same
that he laboured to represent : he so studie
words and sayings brought forth so out
and place to make sport and move laughte
he himself was oftener laughed at than his
were. Yet the foolish fellow brought out now an
then such indifferent and reasonable stuff, that he
made the proverb true, which saith : He that

he thought not of them, so far as we know, but of the Fran-
ciscans whose characteristic virtue is the ' Lady Poverty '
of their founder. (Stapleton, p. 9.) ' The Minorites,' he
wrote, ' unless I am mistaken, yield to none in holiness.'
(Letter to a monk in Jortin's *Erasmus*, ii, 695.) More could
censure abuses, as many saints have done in far stronger
language than his, without any disloyalty to his faith and
the Church. He wrote not for everyone to read, but for the
learned in Latin. It was at a time when the Church was at
peace and when he and his friends had the greatest hopes for
the future from the revival of learning. He would have
written more guardedly if Luther's revolt had already broken
out or could have been foreseen. (It was only a year later,
on October 31, 1517, that Luther posted up on the door of
the Castle Church at Wittenberg his ninety-five theses on
Indulgences. Then events moved quickly and on January 14,
1518, he was excommunicated.) What he says of the
Moria, a sarcastic book which Erasmus composed in
More's own house, he says also of his own works. ' In
these days in which men by their own default, misconstrue,
and take harm of the very scripture of God, until men better
amend, if any man would now translate *Moria* into English,

shooteth oft, at the last shall hit the mark. So that when one of the company said that through my communication a good order was found for thieves, and that the Cardinal also had well provided for vagabonds, so that only remained some good provision to be made for them that through sickness and age were fallen into poverty, and were become so impotent and unwieldy that they were not able to work for their living : " Tush " (quoth he), " let me alone with them : you shall see me do well enough with them. For I had rather than any good, that this kind of people were driven somewhere out of my sight, they have so sore troubled me many times and oft, when they have with their lamentable tears begged money of me : and yet they could never to my mind so tune their song, that thereby they ever got of me one farthing.

or some works either that I have myself written ere this, albeit there be none harm therein, folk yet being (as they are) given to take harm of that that is good, I would not only my darling's (Erasmus's) books but mine own also, help to burn them both with mine own hands, rather than folk should (though through their own fault) take any harm of them, seeing that I see them likely in these days so to do.' (E. W., pp. 422–3.)

Living in times when the Church is constantly attacked by her enemies and thus, so to speak, in a state of siege, we cannot easily throw our minds back to the times when good Catholics could speak us freely as More does of scandals and abuses without failing in reverence to religious institutions. 'I have no doubt,' writes More, as translated by Father Bridgett (p. 99), 'that there is no good man to be found anywhere, to whom all religious orders are not extremely dear and cherished. Not only have I ever loved them, but intensely venerated them.' (For a fuller treatment of the whole matter, see Bridgett, pp. 83 *et seqq.*)

For ever more the one of these two chanced :
either that I would not, or else that I could not,
because I had it not.   Therefore now they be
waxed wise.   For when they see me go by, because
they will not lose their labour, they let me pass and
say not one word to me.   So they look for nothing
of me, no, in good sooth, no more than if I were a
priest or a monk.   But I will make a law that all
these beggars shall be distributed and bestowed
into houses of religion.[1]   The men shall be
made lay brethren, as they call them, and the
women nuns."   Hereat the Cardinal smiled, and
allowed it in jest, yea and all the residue in good
earnest.

'But a certain friar, graduate in divinity, took
such pleasure and delight in this jest of priests and
monks, that he also being else a man of grisly and
stern gravity, began merrily and wantonly to jest
and taunt.   "Nay" (quoth he), "you shall not so
be rid and dispatched of beggars, unless you make
some provision also for us friars."

' "Why" (quoth the jester), "that is done
already, for my lord himself set a very good order
for you, when he decreed that vagabonds should be
kept straight, and set to work : for you be the
greatest and veriest vagabonds that be."

'This jest also, when they saw the Cardinal not
disprove it, every man took it gladly, saving only
the friar.   For he (and that no marvel) being thus
touched on the quick, and hit on the gall, so
fretted, so fumed, and chafed at it, and was in
such a rage, that he could not refrain himself from

---

[1] *houses of religion*.   The original has 'Benedictine
monasteries.'

chiding, scolding, railing, and reviling.[1]   He called
the fellow ribald, villain, javel,[2] backbiter, slanderer,
and the child of perdition, citing therewith terrible
threatenings out of holy scripture.

'Then the jesting scoffer began to play the
scoffer indeed, and verily he was good at that, for
he could play a part in that play no man better.
"Patient yourself, good Master Friar" (quoth he),
"and be not angry, for scripture saith : In your
patience you shall save your souls."[3]

'Then the friar (for I will rehearse his own very
words) : "No, gallous[4] wretch, I am not angry"
(quoth he), "or at the leastwise, I do not sin : for
the Psalmist saith, Be you angry, and sin not."[5]

'Then the Cardinal spoke gently to the friar,
and desired him to quiet himself.

'"No, my lord" (quoth he), "I speak not but
of a good zeal as I ought ; for holy men had a good
zeal. Wherefore it is said : The zeal of thy house
hath eaten me.[6] And it is sung in the church :
The scorners of Helizeus,[7] while he went up into
the house of God, felt the zeal of the bald, as
peradventure this scorning villain ribald shall feel."

'"You do it" (quoth the Cardinal) "perchance

---

[1] *so fretted . . . reviling.* An exaggeration of the simpler
words of the original, ' was so angry and indignant that he
could not refrain from abuse.'

[2] *javel.* A rogue.   [3] *in your patience.* Luke xxi, 19.

[4] *gallous.* Villainous.   [5] *be you angry.* Ps. iv, 5.

[6] *the zeal of thy house.* Ps. lxviii, 10.

[7] *the scorners of Helizeus.* Dr. Lupton prints the original
lines which are found in the hymn of Adam of St. Victor,
De Resurrectione Domini. More pretends that the friar makes
the gross grammatical error of taking *zelus* as a neuter noun.
Cf. 4 Kings ii, 23–4.

of a good mind and affection : but methinketh you
should do, I cannot tell whether more holily,
certainly more wisely, if you would not set your
wit to a fool's wit, and with a fool take in hand a
foolish contention."

' " No, forsooth, my lord " (quoth he), " I
should not do more wisely. For Solomon the
wise saith : Answer a fool according to his folly,[1]
like as I do now, and do show him the pit that he
shall fall into, if he take not heed. For if many
scorners of Helizeus, which was but one bald man,
felt the zeal of the bald, how much more shall one
scorner of many friars feel, among whom be many
bald men ? And we have also the Pope's bulls,
whereby all that mock and scorn us be excommunicated, suspended, and accursed."[2]

' The Cardinal, seeing that no end would be made,
sent away the jester by a privy beck,[3] and turned the
communication to another matter. Shortly after,
when he was risen from the table, he went to hear
his suitors, and so dismissed us.

' Look, Master More, with how long and tedious
a tale I have kept you, which surely I would have
been ashamed to have done, but that you so
earnestly desired me, and did after such a sort give
ear unto it, as though you would not that any
parcel of that communication should be left out.
Which though I have done somewhat briefly, yet
could I not choose but rehearse it, for the judgment
of them which, when they had improved[4] and

---

[1] *answer a fool.* Prov. xxvi, 5.
[2] *suspended and accursed.* These are additions by Robinson.
[3] *privy beck.* A quiet nod of the head.
[4] *improved.* Attacked.

disallowed my sayings, yet incontinent hearing the Cardinal allow them, did themselves also approve the same, so impudently flattering him, that they were nothing ashamed to admit, yea, almost in good earnest, his jester's foolish inventions, because that he himself by smiling at them did seem not to disprove them. So that hereby you may right well perceive how little the courtiers would regard and esteem me and my sayings.'

' I ensure you, Master Raphael,' quoth I, ' I took great delectation in hearing you : all things that you said were spoken so wittily and so pleasantly. And methought myself to be in the meantime, not only at home in my country, but also, through the pleasant remembrance of the Cardinal, in whose house I was brought up of a child, to wax a child again. And, friend Raphael, though I did bear very great love towards you before, yet seeing you do so earnestly favour this man, you will not believe how much my love towards you is now increased.

' But yet, all this notwithstanding, I can by no means change my mind, but that I must needs believe that you, if you be disposed, and can find in your heart to follow some prince's court, shall with your good counsels greatly help and further the commonwealth. Wherefore there is nothing more appertaining to your duty, that is to say, to the duty of a good man. For whereas your Plato[1] judgeth that weal publics shall by this means attain perfect felicity, either if philosophers be kings, or else if kings gave themselves to the study of philosophy, how far, I pray you, shall

[1] *Plato.* Cf. *Republic*, Book V, p. 307.

commonwealths then be from this felicity if philosophers will vouchsafe[1] to instruct kings with their good counsel ? '

' They be not so unkind ' (quoth he), ' but they would gladly do it, yea, many have done it already in books that they have put forth, if kings and princes would be willing and ready to follow good counsel. But Plato[2] doubtless did well foresee, unless kings themselves would apply their minds to the study of philosophy, that else they would never thoroughly allow the counsel of philosophers, being themselves before even from their tender age infected and corrupt with perverse and evil opinions. Which thing Plato himself proved true in King Dionysius. If I should propose to any king wholesome decrees, doing my endeavour to pluck out of his mind the pernicious original causes of vice and naughtiness, think you not that I should forthwith either be driven away, or else made a laughing-stock ?

' Well, suppose I were with the French king, and there sitting in his council, while in that most secret consultation, the king himself there being present in his own person, they beat their brains, and search the very bottoms of their wits, to discuss by what craft and means the king may still keep Milan, and draw to him again fugitive Naples, and then how to conquer the Venetians, and how to bring under his jurisdiction all Italy, then how to win the dominion of Flanders, Brabant, and of all Burgundy, with divers other lands, whose kingdoms

[1] *vouchsafe*. The original has a negative. ' Will not vouchsafe ' gives a clearer meaning.

[2] *Plato*. Cf. *Republic*, Book V, p. 307.

he hath long ago in mind and purpose invaded. Here while one counselleth to conclude a league of peace with the Venetians, so long to endure as shall be thought meet and expedient for their purpose, and to make them also of their council, yea, and besides that to give them part of the prey, which afterward, when they have brought their purpose about after their own minds, they may require and claim again. Another thinketh best to hire the Germans. Another would have the favour of the Swiss won with money. Another's advice is to appease the puissant power of the Emperor's majesty with gold, as with a most pleasant and acceptable sacrifice. While another giveth counsel to make peace with the King of Aragon, and to restore unto him his own kingdom of Navarre as a full assurance of peace. Another cometh in with his five eggs,[1] and adviseth to hook in the King of Castile with some hope of affinity or alliance, and to bring to their part certain peers of his court for great pensions. While they all stay at the chiefest doubt of all, what to do in the meantime with England, and yet agree all in this to make peace with the Englishmen, and with most sure and strong bands to bind that weak and feeble friendship, so that they must be called friends, and had in suspicion as enemies. And that therefore the Scots must be had in readiness, as it were in a standing ready at all occasions, in aunters[2] the

---

[1] *with his five eggs.* An old expression for something worthless. Nothing corresponds to it in the original. The N.E.D. gives the full form of the proverb as ' To come in with five eggs a penny, and four of them addle.'

[2] *in aunters.* In case that.

Englishmen should stir never so little, incontinent to set upon them. And, moreover, privily and secretly (for openly it may not be done by the truce that is taken), privily, thereof, I say, to make much of some peer of England that is banished his country, which must claim title to the crown of the realm, and affirm himself just inheritor thereof, that by this subtle means they may hold to them the king, in whom else they have but small trust and affiance.

' Here, I say, where so great and high matters be in consultation, where so many noble and wise men counsel their king only to war, here if I, silly[1] man, should rise up and will them to turn over the leaf, and learn a new lesson, saying that my counsel is not to meddle with Italy, but to tarry still at home, and that the kingdom of France alone is almost greater than that it may well be governed of one man ; so that the king should not need to study how to get more : and then should propose unto them the decrees of the people that be called the Achoriens,[2] which be situate over against the Island of Utopia on the south-east side.

' These Achoriens once made war in their king's quarrel for to get him another kingdom which he laid claim unto, and advanced himself right inheritor to the crown thereof, by the title of an old alliance. At the last when they had got it, and saw that they had even as much vexation and trouble in keeping it as they had in getting it, and that either their new conquered subjects by sundry occasions were making

---

[1] *silly*. Poor, pitiable.
[2] *Achoriens*. Another imaginary people. From ἀ=not and χώρα=a land.

daily insurrections to rebel against them, or else that other countries were continually with diverse inroads and foragings invading them ; so that they were ever fighting either for them or against them, and never could break up their camps : seeing themselves in the mean season pilled and impoverished ; their money carried out of the realm ; their own men killed to maintain the glory of another nation ; when they had no war, peace nothing better than war, by reason that their people in war had so inured themselves to corrupt and wicked manners ; that they had taken a delight and pleasure in robbing and stealing ; that through manslaughter they had gathered boldness to mischief ; that their laws were had in contempt, and nothing set by or regarded ; that their king being troubled with the charge and governance of two kingdoms, could not nor was not able perfectly to discharge his office towards them both ; seeing again that all these evils and troubles were endless ; at the last laid their heads together, and like faithful and loving subjects gave to their king free choice and liberty to keep still the one of these two kingdoms whether he would ; alleging that he was not able to keep both, and that they were more than might well be governed of half a king ; forasmuch as no man would be content to take him for his muleteer that keepeth another man's mules besides his. So this good prince was constrained to be content with his old kingdom, and to give over the new to one of his friends, who shortly after was violently driven out.

'Furthermore, if I should declare unto them that all this busy preparation for war, whereby so many

nations for his sake should be brought into a
troublesome hurly-burly, when all his coffers were
emptied, his treasures wasted, and his people
destroyed, should at the length through some mis-
chance be in vain and to none effect ; and that
therefore it were best for him to content himself
with his own kingdom of France, as his forefathers
and predecessors did before him, to make much of
it, to enrich it, and to make it as flourishing as he
could, to endeavour himself to love his subjects,
and again to be beloved of them, willingly to live
with them, peaceably to govern them, and with
other kingdoms not to meddle, seeing that which
he hath already is even enough for him, yea and
more than he can well turn him to ; this mine
advice, Master More, how think you it would be
heard and taken ? '

' So God help me[1] not very thankfully,' quoth I.

' Well, let us proceed then,' quoth he. ' Suppose
that some king and his council were together
whetting their wits[2] and devising what subtle
craft they might invent to enrich the king with
great treasures of money. First one counselleth to
raise and enhance the valuation of money when the
king must pay any ; and again to call down the
value of coin to less than it is worth when he must
receive or gather any. For thus great sums shall
be paid with a little money, and where little is
due, much shall be received. Another counselleth

---

[1] *So God help me.* Another addition of the translator.

[2] *whetting their wits.* Every one of the devices which
follow either had been employed or was later to be employed
in England. See details in the notes of Dr. Lupton and
Churton Collins.

to feign war, that when under this colour and pretence the king hath gathered great abundance of money, he may, when it shall please him, make peace with great solemnity and holy ceremonies, to blind the eyes of the poor commonalty, as taking pity and compassion forsooth upon man's blood, like a loving and a merciful prince. Another putteth the king in remembrance of certain old and moth-eaten laws, that of long time have not been put in execution, which because no man can remember that they were made, every man hath transgressed. The fines of these laws he counselleth the king to require; for there is no way so profitable, nor more honourable, as the which hath a show and colour of justice. Another adviseth him to forbid many things under great penalties and fines, specially such things as is for the people's profit not be used, and afterwards to dispense for money with them which by this prohibition sustain loss and damage. For by this means the favour of the people is won, and profit riseth two ways. First by taking forfeits of them whom covetousness of gains hath brought in danger of this statute, and also by selling privileges and licences, which the better that the prince is forsooth, the dearer he selleth them; as one that is loath to grant to any private person anything that is against the profit of his people. And therefore may sell none but at an exceeding dear price.

'Another giveth the king counsel to endanger unto his grace the judges of the realm, that he may have them ever on his side, and that they may in every matter dispute and reason for the king's right. Yea, and further to call them into his

palace and to require them there to argue and
discuss his matters in his own presence. So there
shall be no matter of his so openly wrong and
unjust, wherein one or other of them, either
because he will have something to allege and
object, or that he is ashamed to say that which is
said already, or else to pick a thank with his prince,
will not find some hole open to set a snare in,
wherewith to take the contrary part in a trip. Thus
whilst the judges cannot agree amongst themselves,
reasoning and arguing of that which is plain
enough, and bringing the manifest truth in doubt;
in the mean season the king may take a fit occasion
to understand the law as shall most make for his
advantage, whereunto all other for shame or for
fear will agree. Then the judges may be bold to
pronounce on the king's side. For he that giveth
sentence for the king cannot be without a good
excuse. For it shall be sufficient for him to have
equity on his part, or the bare words of the law,
or a written and wrested understanding of the
same, or else, which with good and just judges
is of greater force than all laws be, the king's
indisputable prerogative.

'To conclude, all the counsellors agree and
consent together with the rich Crassus, that no
abundance of gold can be sufficient for a prince,
which must keep and maintain an army : furthermore that a king, though he would, can do nothing
unjustly. For all that all men have, yea also the men
themselves, be all his. And that every man hath
so much of his own as the king's gentleness hath
not taken from him. And that it shall be most for
the king's advantage that his subjects have very

little or nothing in their possession, as whose
safeguard doth herein consist, that his people do
not wax wanton and wealthy through riches and
liberty, because where these things be, there men
be not wont patiently to obey hard, unjust, and
unlawful commandments ; whereas, on the other
part, need and poverty doth hold down and keep
under stout courages, and maketh them patient
perforce, taking from them bold and rebelling
stomachs.

' Here again, if I should rise up and boldly
affirm that all these counsels be to the king dis-
honour and reproach, whose honour and safety is
more and rather supported and upholden by the
wealth and riches of his people than by his own
treasures ; and if I should declare that the commonalty chooseth their king for their own sake,
and not for his sake ;[1] to the intent, that through

---

[1] *The king for their own sake and not for his sake.* ' This
conception of kingship is essentially medieval and reflects
the teaching of St. Thomas Aquinas who wrote in the
Summa and again in the *De Regimine Principum* of a twofold
style of kingship ; one the *regimen regale*, which is absolute
monarchy, and the other, *regimen regale et politicum*, which
is constitutional monarchy. This distinction made by
St. Thomas was formally taken up (with acknowledgment)
and applied to the English Constitution by Sir John
Fortescue, a fifteenth-century Chief Justice and author of
the first treatise on the English Constitution, *De Laudibus
Legum Angliae*. It is interesting to recall that the (like but
less formal) teaching of Bracton in the thirteenth century
and of Fortescue in the fifteenth century was used by the
lawyers and the Parliamentarians of the seventeenth century
in their attempt to overthrow the doctrine of the divine
right of kings which James I had introduced.' I owe this
note to Mr. R. O'Sullivan.

his labour and study they might all live wealthily safe from wrongs and injuries ; and that therefore the king ought to take more care for the wealth of his people than for his own wealth, even as the office and duty of a shepherd is, in that he is a shepherd, to feed his sheep rather than himself.[1]

'For as touching this, that they think the defence

---

[1] *his sheep rather than himself.* ' Wo to the shepherds of Israel that fed themselves : should not the flocks be fed by the shepherds.' (*Ezech.* xxxiv, 2.) The responsibilities of kings and other rulers are constantly insisted on in Holy Scripture. ' Have they made thee ruler ? Be not lifted up : be among them as one of them. Have care of them.' (*Ecclus.* xxxii, 1.) ' Mercy and truth preserve the king, and his throne is strengthened by clemency.' (*Prov.* xx, 28.) See also *Wisdom* vi, 2 ; *Ps.* ii, 10 ; *Jer.* xiii, 1, etc. St. Thomas Aquinas distinguishes four kinds of legitimate systems of government, kingship, aristocracy, oligarchy, and democracy. He adds a fifth system (tyranny) which he says is utterly corrupt and not the basis of a just law (Ia–IIae, Q. xcvi). The best form of government he declares (*ibid.*, Q. cv) to be an admixture of kingship ' in as much as one has the chief power,' aristocracy ' in as much as many have subordinate authority,' and democracy, ' i.e. the power of the people in as much as the princes may be chosen from the ranks of the people, and the people have the right of electing them.' Such an ideal government he finds among the Jews of the Old Testament. Elsewhere (IIa–IIae, Q. lxvi, a. 8) he teaches that if princes unjustly deprive others of their goods, whether their own subjects or their adversaries in an unjust war, they sin and are bound to restitution. In this matter he quotes from St. Augustine. ' If justice is set aside, what are kingdoms but robberies on a large scale, and what are robberies but kingdoms on a small scale.' (*De Civ. Dei*, iv, 4.) These passages may well have been in St. Thomas's mind, as well as Plato's words, comparing kings to shepherds and tyrannies to wholesale robbery. (*Republic*, Book 1, p. 164).

and maintenance of peace to consist in the poverty of the people, the thing itself showeth that they be far out of the way. For where shall a man find more wrangling, quarrelling, brawling, and chiding, than among beggars? Who be more desirous of new mutations and alterations, than they that be not content with the present state of their life? Or, finally, who be bolder stomached to bring all in a hurly-burly (thereby trusting to get some windfall) than they that have now nothing to lose? And if any king were so smally regarded, and so lightly esteemed, yea, so behated of his subjects, that other ways he could not keep them in awe, but only by open wrongs, by polling and shaving, and by bringing them to beggary, surely it were better for him to forsake his kingdom,[1] than to hold it by this means; whereby though the name of a king be kept, yet the majesty is lost; for it is against the dignity of a king to have rule over beggars, but rather over rich and wealthy men. Of this mind was the hardy and courageous Fabricius,[2] when he said that he had rather be a ruler of rich men than be rich himself. And verily one man to live in pleasure and wealth, whilst all others weep and smart for it, that is the part, not of a king, but of a jailer.

' To be short, as he is a foolish physician that cannot cure his patient's disease unless he cast him

[1] *forsake his kingdom.* Compare the well-known words of St. Edward the Confessor, with which More will have been familiar, that he would prefer to forgo a kingdom which could not be obtained without bloodshed.

[2] *Fabricius.* More seems to have given his name in mistake for M. Curius Dentatus, to whom the saying is ascribed in *Valerius Maximus*, iv, 5.

in another sickness, so he that cannot amend the
lives of his subjects but by taking from them the
wealth and commodity of life, he must needs gran.
that he knoweth not the feat how to government
But let him rather amend his own life, renounce
unhonest pleasures, and forsake pride. For these
be the chief vices that cause him to run in the
contempt or hatred of his people. Let him live
of his own, hurting no man. Let him do cost not
above[1] his power. Let him restrain wickedness.
Let him prevent vices, and take away the occasions
of offences by well ordering his subjects, and not
by suffering wickedness to increase afterward to be
punished. Let him not be too hasty in calling again
laws which a custom hath abrogated : specially
such as have been long forgotten, and never lacked
nor needed. And let him never, under the cloak
and pretence of transgression, take such fines and
forfeits as no judge will suffer a private person to
take, as unjust and full of guile.

'Here if I should bring forth before them the
law of the Macariens,[2] which be not far distant from
Utopia ; whose king the day of his coronation is
bound by a solemn oath, that he shall never at any
time have in his treasure above a thousand pound
of gold or silver. They say a very good king,
which took more care for the wealth and commodity
of his country than for the enriching of himself,
made this law to be a stop and a bar to kings from
heaping and hoarding up so much money as might

[1] *Do cost not above.* The Latin means 'let him measure
his expenses by his income.'

[2] *Macariens.* Another feigned people, the name being
derived from ' μάκαρες,' happy.

impoverish their people. For he foresaw that this sum of treasure would suffice to support the king in battle against his own people, if they should chance to rebel; and also to maintain his wars against the invasions of his foreign enemies. Again, he perceived the same stock of money to be too little and insufficient to encourage and enable him wrongfully to take away other men's goods: which was the chief cause why the law was made. Another cause was this. He thought that by this provision his people should not lack money wherewith to maintain their daily occupying and chaffer. And seeing the king could not choose but lay out and bestow all that came in above the prescript sum of his stock, he thought he would seek no occasions to do his subjects injury. Such a king shall be feared of evil men, and loved of good men. These, and such other informations, if I should use among men wholly inclined and given to the contrary part, how deaf hearers, think you, should I have?'

'Deaf hearers doubtless' (quoth I), 'and in good faith no marvel. And to be plain with you, truly I cannot allow that such communication shall be used, or such counsel given, as you be sure shall never be regarded nor received. For how can so strange informations be profitable, or how can they be beaten into their heads, whose minds be already prevented with clean contrary persuasions? This school philosophy is not unpleasant among friends in familiar communication, but in the counsels of kings, where great matters be debated and reasoned with great authority, these things have no place.'

'That is it which I meant' (quoth he), 'when
I said philosophy had no place among kings.'

'Indeed' (quoth I), 'this school philosophy hath
not : which thinketh all things meet for every
place. But there is another philosophy more civil,
which knoweth, as ye would say, her own stage,
and thereafter ordering and behaving herself in
the play that she hath in hand, playeth her part
accordingly with comeliness, uttering nothing out
of due order and fashion. And this is the philosophy
that you must use. Or else whilst a comedy of
Plautus is playing, and the vile bondmen scoffing
and trifling among themselves, if you should
suddenly come upon the stage in a philosopher's
apparel, and rehearse out of Octavia the place
wherein Seneca disputeth with Nero ; had it not
been better for you to have played the dumb person,
than by rehearsing that which served neither for
the time nor place, to have made such a tragical
comedy or gallimaufry ? For by bringing in other
stuff that nothing appertaineth to the present
matter, you must needs mar and pervert the play
that is in hand, though the stuff that you bring be
much better. What part soever you have taken
upon you, play that as well as you can and make the
best of it. And do not therefore disturb and bring
out of order the whole matter, because that another,
which is merrier and better, cometh to your
remembrance.

'So the case standeth in a commonwealth, and
so it is in the consultations of kings and princes.
If evil opinions and naughty persuasions cannot
be utterly and quite plucked out of their hearts,
if you cannot even as you would remedy vices

which use and custom hath confirmed; yet for this cause you must not leave and forsake the commonwealth. You must not forsake the ship in a tempest, because you cannot rule and keep down the winds. No, nor you must not labour to drive into their heads new and strange informations, which you know well shall be nothing regarded with them that be of clean contrary minds. But you must with a crafty wile and a subtle train study and endeavour yourself, as much as in you lieth, to handle the matter wittily and handsomely for the purpose, and that which you cannot turn to good, so to order it that it be not very bad. For it is not possible for all things to be well, unless all men were good. Which I think will not be yet these good many years.'

'By this means' (quoth he) 'nothing else will be brought to pass, but while that I go about to remedy the madness of others, I should be even as mad as they. For if I would speak such things that be true I must needs speak such things: but as for to speak false things, whether that be a philosopher's part or no I cannot tell, truly it is not my part. Howbeit this communication of mine, though peradventure it may seem unpleasant to them, yet can I not see why it should seem strange, or foolishly new-fangled. If so be that I should speak those things that Plato feigneth in his weal public, or that the Utopians do in theirs, these things, though they were (as they be indeed) better, yet they might seem spoken out of place. Forasmuch as here among us, every man hath his possessions several to himself, and there all things be common.

'But what was in my communication contained, that might not, and ought not, in any place to be spoken? Saving that to them which have thoroughly decreed and determined with themselves to run headlong the contrary way, it cannot be acceptable and pleasant, because it calleth them back and showeth them the jeopardies. Verily, if all things that evil and vicious manners have caused to seem inconvenient and naught should be refused, as things unmeet and reproachful, then we must among Christian people wink at the most part of all those things which Christ taught us, and so straightly forbade them to be winked at, that those things also which He whispered in the ears of His disciples He commanded to be proclaimed in open houses.[1] And yet the most part of them are more dissident from the manners of the world nowadays than my communication was.

'But preachers, sly and wily men, following your counsel (as I suppose), because they saw men evil-willing to frame their manners to Christ's rule, they have wrested and wryed His doctrine, and like a rule of lead[2] have applied it to men's manners ; that by some means at the least way, they might agree together. Whereby I cannot see what good they have done, but that men may more sickerly[3] be evil. And I truly should prevail even as little in kings' councils. For either I must say otherwise than they say, and then I were as good to say

---

[1] *in open houses.* On the house-tops. A reference to *Matt.* x, 27, 'That which I tell you in the dark, speak ye in the light : and that which you hear in the ear, preach ye upon the house-tops.'

[2] *rule of lead.* Therefore pliable, easily bent.

[3] *sickerly.* Surely.

nothing, or else I must say the same that they say, and (as Mitio saith in Terence[1]) help to further their madness. For that crafty wile and subtle train[2] of yours, I cannot perceive to what purpose it serveth, wherewith you would have me to study and endeavour myself, if all things cannot be made good, yet to handle them wittily and handsomely for the purpose, that as far forth as is possible they may not be very evil. For there is no place to dissemble in, nor to wink in. Naughty counsels must be openly allowed, and very pestilent decrees must be approved. He shall be counted worse than a spy, yea, almost as evil as a traitor, that with a faint heart doth praise evil and noisome decrees.

' Moreover, a man can have no occasion to do good, chancing into the company of them, which will sooner pervert a good man, than be made good themselves ; through whose evil company he shall be marred, or else if he remain good and innocent, yet the wickedness and folly of others shall be imputed to him, and laid in his neck. So that it is impossible with that crafty wile and subtle train to turn anything to better.

' Wherefore Plato,[3] by a goodly similitude, declareth why wise men refrain to meddle in the commonwealth. For when they see the people swarm into the streets, and daily wet to the skin with rain, and yet cannot persuade them to go out of the rain, and to take their houses, knowing well that if they should go out to them, they should

---

[1] *Terence*. In the *Adelphi*, i, 2, 67.

[2] *train*. Artifice.

[3] *Plato*. The ' goodly similitude ' is in the *Republic*, Book VI, p. 330. More gives it in his own words.

nothing prevail, nor win aught by it, but with them be wet also in the rain, they do keep themselves within their houses, being content that they be safe themselves, seeing they cannot remedy the folly of the people.

'Howbeit, doubtless, Master More (to speak truly as my mind giveth me), where possessions be private, where money beareth all the stroke, it is hard and almost impossible that there the weal public may justly be governed and prosperously flourish. Unless you think thus : that Justice is there executed, where all things come into the hands of evil men, or that prosperity there flourisheth, where all is divided among a few ; which few nevertheless do not lead their lives very wealthily, and the residue live miserably, wretchedly, and beggarly.

'Wherefore when I consider with myself and weigh in my mind the wise and godly ordinances of the Utopians, among whom, with very few laws, all things be so well and wealthily ordered, that virtue is had in prize and estimation, and yet all things being there common, every man hath abundance of everything. Again, on the other part, when I compare with them so many nations ever making new laws, yet none of them all well and sufficiently furnished with laws ; where every man calleth that he hath gotten his own proper and private goods, where so many new laws daily made be not sufficient for every man to enjoy, defend, and know from another man's that which he calleth his own ; which thing the infinite controversies in the law, daily rising, never to be ended, plainly declare to be true.

' These things (I say), when I consider with myself, I hold well with Plato,[1] and do nothing marvel, that he would make no laws for them that refused those laws whereby all men should have and enjoy equal portions of wealth and commodities. For the wise man did easily foresee this to be the one and only way to the wealth of a community, if equality of all things should be brought in and established. Which I think is not possible to be observed where every man's goods be proper and peculiar to himself. For where every man under certain titles and pretences draweth and plucketh to himself as much as he can, so that a few divide among themselves all the whole riches, be there never so much abundance and store, there to the residue is left lack and poverty. And for the most part it chanceth that this latter sort is more worthy to enjoy that state of wealth, than the other be ; because the rich men be covetous, crafty, and unprofitable. On the other part, the poor be lowly, simple, and by their daily labour more profitable to the commonwealth than to themselves.

' Thus I do fully persuade myself that no equal and just distribution of things can be made, nor that perfect wealth shall ever be among men, unless this propriety be exiled and banished. But so long as it shall continue, so long shall remain among the most and best part of men the heavy and inevitable burden of poverty and wretchedness. Which, as I grant that it may be somewhat eased so I utterly deny that it can wholly be taken away. For if there were a statute made, that no man

[1] *Plato*. The story is given by Diogenes Laertius in his *Lives of Famous Philosophers*, iii, 27.

should possess above a certain measure of ground,
and that no man should have in his stock above a
prescript and appointed sum of money ; if it were
by certain laws decreed, that neither the king should
be of too great power, neither the people too
haughty and wealthy, and that offices should not
be obtained by inordinate suit, or by bribes and
gifts ; that they should neither be bought nor sold,
nor that it should be needful for the officers to be
at any cost or charge in their offices ; for so
occasion is given to them by fraud and ravin to
gather up their money again, and by reason of
gifts and bribes the offices be given to rich men,
which should rather have been executed of wise
men : by such laws, I say, like as sick bodies that
be desperate and past cure, be wont with continual
good cherishing to be kept and botched up for
a time ; so these evils also might be lightened and
mitigated. But that they may be perfectly cured,
and brought to a good and upright state, it is not
to be hoped for whiles every man is master of his
own to himself. Yea, and whiles you go about to
do your cure of one part, you shall make bigger
the sore of another part, so the help of one
causeth another's harm ; forasmuch as nothing
can be given to anyone, unless it be taken from
another.'

  ' But I am of a contrary opinion ' (quoth I), ' for
methinketh that men shall never there live wealthily
where all things be common. For how can there
be abundance of goods, or of anything, where every
man withdraweth his hand from labour ? Whom
the regard of his own gains driveth not to work,
but the hope that he hath in other men's travails

maketh him slothful.[1] Then when they be pricked
with poverty, and yet no man can by any law or
right defend that for his own, which he hath gotten
with the labour of his own hands, shall not there
of necessity be continual sedition and bloodshed ?
Specially the authority and reverence of magistrates
being taken away, which, what place it may have
with such men among whom is no difference,
I cannot devise.'

' I marvel not ' (quoth he) ' that you be of this
opinion. For you conceive in your mind either
none at all, or else a very false image and similitude
of this thing. But if you had been with me in
Utopia, and had presently seen their fashions and
laws, as I did, which lived there five years, and more,
and would never have come hence, but only to
make that new land known here ; then, doubtless,
you would grant that you never saw people well
ordered, but only there.'

' Surely ' (quoth Master Peter) ' it shall be hard
for you to make me believe that there is better order
in that new land than is here in these countries
that we know. For good wits be as well here as
there ; and I think our commonwealths be ancienter
than theirs ; wherein long use and experience hath
found out many things commodious for man's life,
besides that many things here among us have been

---

[1] *slothful*. More pricks the bubble of Hythloday's airy
speculations with a recall to the realities of life. Com-
munistic schemes demand that men should work as zealously
for the common weal as they do for their own gain. As
he said a few pages back : ' It is not possible for all things
to be well, unless all men were good. Which I think will
not be yet this good many years.' (See too Introduction,
p. xxv).

found by chance, which no wit could ever have devised.'

' As touching the ancientness ' (quoth he) ' of commonwealths, then you might better judge, if you had read the histories and chronicles of that land, which if we may believe, cities were there, before men were here. Now what thing soever hitherto by wit hath been devised, or found by chance, that might be as well there as here. But I think verily, though it were so that we did pass them in wit, yet in study, in travail, and in laboursome endeavour they far pass us. For (as their chronicles testify) before our arrival there, they never heard anything of us, whom they call the ultraequinoctials ; saving that once, about twelve hundred years ago, a certain ship was lost by the Isle of Utopia which was driven thither by tempest. Certain Romans and Egyptians were cast on land, which after that never went thence.

' Mark now what profit they took of this one occasion through diligence and earnest travail. There was no craft nor science within the Empire of Rome whereof any profit could rise, but they either learned it of these strangers, or else of them taking occasion to search for it, found it out. So great profit was it to them that ever any went thither from hence. But if any like chance before this hath brought any man from thence hither, that is as quite out of remembrance, as this also perchance in time to come shall be forgotten, that ever I was there. And like as they quickly, almost at the first meeting, made their own, whatsoever is among us wealthily devised ; so I suppose it would be long before we would receive anything that among them is better instituted than among us. And this I suppose is the chief cause why their commonwealths be wiselier governed, and do flourish in more wealth than ours, though we neither in wit nor riches be their inferiors.'

'Therefore, gentle Master Raphael' (quoth I), 'I pray you and beseech you describe unto us the island. And study not to be short; but declare largely in order their grounds, their rivers, their cities, their people, their manners, their ordinances, their laws, and, to be short, all things that you shall think us desirous to know. And you shall think us desirous to know whatsoever we know not yet.'

'There is nothing' (quoth he) 'that I will do gladlier. For all these things I have fresh in mind. But the matter requireth leisure.'

'Let us go in, therefore' (quoth I), 'to dinner, afterward we will bestow the time at our pleasure.'

'Content' (quoth he) 'be it.'

So we went in and dined. When dinner was done we came into the same place again, and sat us down upon the same bench, commanding our servants that no man should trouble us. Then I and Master Peter Giles desired Master Raphael to perform his promise. He, therefore, seeing us desirous and willing to hearken to him, when he had sat still and paused a little while, musing and bethinking himself, thus be began to speak.

THE END OF THE FIRST BOOK

THE SECOND BOOK

OF THE COMMUNICATION OF RAPHAEL
HYTHLODAY, CONCERNING THE BEST
STATE OF A COMMONWEALTH CONTAIN-
ING THE DESCRIPTION OF UTOPIA, WITH
A LARGE DECLARATION OF THE POLITIC
GOVERNMENT, AND OF ALL THE GOOD
LAWS AND ORDERS OF THE SAME
ISLAND

THE DESCRIPTION OF UTOPIA

THE Island of Utopia containeth in breadth in the middle part of it (for there it is broadest) two hundred miles. Which breadth continueth through the most part of the land, saving that by little and little it cometh in and waxeth narrower towards both the ends. Which fetching about a circuit or compass of five hundred miles,[1] do fashion the whole island like to the new moon. Between these two corners the sea runneth in, dividing them asunder by the distance of eleven miles or thereabouts, and there surmounteth[2] into a large and wide sea, which by reason that the land on every side compasseth it about, and sheltereth it from the winds, is not rough, nor mounteth not with great waves, but almost floweth quietly, not much unlike a great standing pool; and maketh well-nigh all the space within the belly of the land in manner of a haven; and to the great commodity of the inhabitants receiveth in ships towards every part of the land. The forefronts or frontiers of the

[1] *a compass of five hundred miles.* Utopia is a land five hundred miles long and two hundred broad, tapering towards each end. These ends are conceived as being bent round towards each other until they are but eleven miles apart. The whole is in the form of the crescent moon within the horns of which is an enormous natural harbour.

[2] *surmounteth.* Behind the corners the water forms a wide sea.

two corners, what with fords and shelves, and what
with rocks, be very jeopardous and dangerous. In
the middle distance between them both standeth
up above the water a great rock, which therefore
is nothing perilous because it is in sight. Upon
the top of this rock is a fair and a strong tower
built, which they hold with a garrison of men.
Other rocks there be lying hid under the water,
which therefore be dangerous. The channels be
known only to themselves. And therefore it
seldom chanceth that any stranger, unless he be
guided by an Utopian, can come into this haven.
Insomuch that they themselves could scarcely enter
without jeopardy, but that their way is directed
and ruled by certain landmarks standing on the
shore. By turning, translating, and removing these
marks into other places they may destroy their
enemies' navies, be they ever so many. The outside
or utter circuit of the land is also full of havens,
but the landing is so surely fenced, what by nature,
and what by workmanship of man's hand, that a
few defenders may drive back many armies.

Howbeit as they say, and as the fashion of the
place itself doth partly show, it was not ever
compassed about with the sea. But King Utopus,
whose name, as conqueror, the island beareth (for
before his time it was called Abraxa), which also
brought the rude and wild people to that excellent
perfection in all good fashions, humanity, and civil
gentleness, wherein they now go beyond all the
people of the world ; even at his first arriving and
entering upon the land, forthwith obtaining the
victory, caused fifteen miles' space of uplandish
ground, where the sea had no passage, to be cut

and digged up, and so brought the sea round about the land. He set to this work not only the inhabitants of the island (because they should not think it done in contumely and despite), but also all his own soldiers. Thus the work being divided into so great a number of workmen, was with exceeding marvellous speed dispatched. Insomuch that the borderers, which at the first began to mock and to jest at this vain enterprise, then turned their derision to marvel at the success, and to fear.

There be in the island fifty-four large and fair cities, or shire towns,[1] agreeing altogether in one tongue, in like manners, institutions, and laws. They be all set and situated alike, and in all points fashioned alike, as far north as the place or plot suffereth. Of these cities they that be nighest together be twenty-four miles asunder. Again there is none of them distant from the next above one day's journey on foot.

There come yearly to Amaurote[2] out of every city three old men, wise and well experienced, there to entreat and debate of the common matters of the land. For this city (because it standeth just in the

[1] *shire towns.* The number of counties in England and Wales has been variously reckoned at various times, but it is not far from fifty-four. In much of his description More clearly has England in view, though it is not always easy to say whether it is England as it was in his day or the ideal England of his dreams. Erasmus writes in the letter to von Hutten : ' He published the *Utopia* to show the causes why states were not prosperous, but it was Britain in particular that he depicted, for he has a deep and thorough knowledge of that State.'

[2] *Amaurote.* From ἀμαυρός dim, obscure. It is London, with the qualification expressed in the previous note.

middle of the island, and is therefore most meet for
the ambassadors of all parts of the realm) is taken
for the chief and head city. The precincts and
bounds of the shires be so commodiously appointed
out, and set forth for the cities, that none of them
all hath of any side less than twenty miles of ground,
and of some side also much more, as of that part
where the cities be of farther distance asunder.
None of the cities desire to enlarge the bounds and
limits of their shires. For they count themselves
rather the good husbands, than the owners of their
lands.

They have in the country in all parts of the shire
houses or farms built, well appointed and furnished
with all sorts of instruments and tools belonging
to husbandry. These houses be inhabited of the
citizens, which come thither to dwell by course.
No household or farm in the country hath fewer
than forty persons, men and women, besides two
bondmen, which be all under the rule and order
of the good-man and the good-wife of the house,
being both very sage, discreet, and ancient persons.
And every thirty farms or families have one head
ruler, which is called a Philarch,[1] being as it were, a
head bailiff. Out of every one of these families
or farms cometh every year into the city twenty
persons which have continued two years before
in the country. In their place so many fresh be
sent thither out of the city, who, of them that have
been there a year already, and be therefore expert
and cunning in husbandry, shall be instructed and
taught. And they the next year shall teach other.
This order is used for fear that either scarceness of

---

[1] *Philarch.* From φυλή and ἀρκός=ruler of a tribe.

victuals, or some other like incommodity should chance, through lack of knowledge, if they should be altogether new, and fresh, and unexpert in husbandry. This manner and fashion of yearly changing and renewing the occupiers of husbandry, though it be solemn and customably used, to the intent that no man shall be constrained against his will to continue long in that hard and sharp kind of life, yet many of them have such a pleasure and delight in husbandry, that they obtain a longer space of years. These husbandmen plough and till the ground, and breed up cattle, and provide and make ready wood, which they carry to the city either by land, or by water, as they may most conveniently.

They bring up a great multitude of pulleyn,[1] and that by a marvellous policy. For the hens do not sit upon the eggs, but by keeping them in a certain equal heat they bring life into them, and hatch them. The chickens, as soon as they become out of the shell, follow men[2] and women instead of the hens.

They bring up very few horses, nor none but very fierce ones; and that for none other use or purpose, but only to exercise their youth in riding and feats of arms. For oxen be put to all the labour of ploughing and drawing. Which they grant to be not so good as horses at a sudden brunt, and (as we say) at a dead lift, but yet they hold opinion, that oxen will abide and suffer much more labour,

[1] *pulleyn*. Poultry.
[2] *follow men*. References to artificial incubation are not unknown in earlier writers, but this last touch is More's own fancy.

pain, and hardness, than horses will. And they think that oxen be not in danger and subject unto so many diseases, and that they be kept and maintained with much less cost and charge ; and, finally, that they be good for meat when they be past labour.

They sow corn only for bread. For their drink is either wine made of grapes, or else of apples, or pears, or else it is clear water. And many times mead made of honey or liquorice sodden in water, for thereof they have great store. And though they know certainly (for they know it perfectly indeed) how much victuals the city with the whole country or shire round about it doth spend, yet they sow much more corn, and breed up much more cattle, than serveth for their own use, parting the overplus among their borderers. Whatsoever necessary things be lacking in the country, all such stuff they fetch out of the city ; where without any exchange they easily obtain it of the magistrates of the city. For every month many of them go into the city on the holy day. When their harvest day draweth near, and is at hand, then the Philarchs, which be the head officers and bailiffs of husbandry, send word to the magistrates of the city what number of harvestmen is needful to be sent to them out of the city. The which company of harvestmen being ready at the day appointed, almost in one fair day dispatcheth all the harvest work.

OF THE CITIES AND NAMELY OF AMAUROTE

AS for their cities, whoso knoweth one of them, knoweth them all : they be all so like one to another, as far forth as the nature of the place permitteth. I will describe, therefore, to you one or other of them, for it skilleth not greatly which ; but which rather than Amaurote ? Of them all this is the worthiest and of most dignity. For the residue acknowledge it for the head city, because there is the council-house. Nor to me any of them all is better beloved, as wherein I lived five whole years together. The city of Amaurote standeth upon the side of a low hill, in fashion almost four-square. For the breadth of it beginneth a little beneath the top of the hill, and still continueth by the space of two miles, until it come to the river of Anyder.[1] The length of it, which lieth by the riverside, is somewhat more.

The river of Anyder riseth four and twenty miles above Amaurote out of a little spring. But being increased by other small rivers and brooks that run into it, and among other two somewhat big ones, before the city it is half a mile broad, and farther broader. And forty miles beyond the city it falleth into the ocean sea. By all that space[2] that

[1] *Anyder*. From ἀ–(ν) and ὕδωρ = without water.
[2] *all that space*. A note in the margin of the original states that this occurs in the Thames.

lieth between the sea and the city, and certain miles
also above the city, the water ebbeth and floweth
six hours together with a swift tide. When the
sea floweth in, for the length of thirty miles, it
filleth all the Anyder with salt water, and driveth
back the fresh water of the river. And somewhat
further it changeth the sweetness of the fresh water
with saltness. But a little beyond that the river
waxeth sweet, and runneth forby the city fresh and
pleasant. And when the sea ebbeth and goeth
back again, the fresh water followeth it almost even
to the very fall into the sea.

There goeth a bridge over the river made not
of piles or of timber, but of stonework, with
gorgeous and substantial arches at that part of
the city that is farthest from the sea ; to the intent
that ships may pass along forby all the side of the
city without let.

They have also another river¹ which, indeed, is
not very great. But it runneth gently and pleasantly.
For it riseth even out of the same hill that the city
standeth upon, and runneth down a slope through
the midst of the city into Anyder. And because it
riseth a little without the city, the Amaurotians
have enclosed the head-spring of it with strong
fences and bulwarks, and so have joined it to the
city. This is done to the intent that the water
should not be stopped, nor turned away, nor
poisoned, if their enemies should chance to come
upon them. From thence the water is derived and
conveyed down in channels of brick divers ways
into the lower parts of the city. Where that cannot

¹ *another river*. Like the Fleet river in London, not yet
in More's day ingloriously hidden in sewers.

be done, by reason that the place will not suffer it, there they gather the rain-water in great cisterns, which doeth them as good service.

The city is compassed about with a high and thick stone wall full of turrets and bulwarks. A dry ditch, but deep, and broad, and overgrown with bushes, briers, and thorns, goeth about three sides or quarters of the city. To the fourth side the river itself serveth for a ditch. The streets be appointed and set forth very commodious and handsome, both for carriage, and also against the winds. The houses be of fair and gorgeous building, and on the street side they stand joined together in a long row, through the whole street, without any partition or separation. The streets be twenty feet broad. On the back side of the houses, through the whole length of the street, lie large gardens enclosed round about with the back part of the streets. Every house hath two doors, one into the street, and a postern door on the back side into the garden. These doors be made with two leaves, never locked[1] nor bolted, so easy to be opened, that they will follow the least drawing of a finger, and shut again alone. Whoso will, may go in, for there is nothing within the houses that is private, or any man's own. And every tenth year they change their houses by lot.

They set great store by their gardens.[2] In them

---

[1] *never locked.* A marginal note in the Latin refers us to Plato's community of goods. Cf. *Republic*, Book III, p. 244.

[2] *gardens.* It should be noted that these were not partitioned off for each house, but common to all the dwellers of the street, something like the gardens in the squares of modern London.

they have vineyards,[1] all manner of fruit, herbs, and flowers, so pleasant, so well furnished, and so finely kept, that I never saw thing more fruitful nor better trimmed in any place. Their study and diligence herein cometh not only of pleasure, but also of a certain strife and contention that is between street and street concerning the trimming, husbanding, and furnishing of their gardens; every man for his own part. And verily you shall not lightly find in all the city anything that is more commodious, either for the profit of the citizens or for pleasure. And, therefore, it may seem that the first founder of the city minded nothing so much as these gardens. For they say that King Utopus himself, even at the first beginning, appointed and drew forth the platform[2] of the city into this fashion and figure that it hath now, but the gallant garnishing, and the beautiful setting forth of it, whereunto he saw that one man's age would not suffice: that he left to his posterity. For their chronicles, which they keep written with all diligent circumspection, containing the history of one thousand seven hundred and sixty years, even from the first conquest of the island, record and witness that the houses in the beginning were very low, and like homely cottages or poor shepherd houses, made, at all adventures, of every rude piece of timber that came first to hand, with mud walls, and ridged roofs thatched over with straw. But now the houses be curiously built, after a gorgeous and gallant sort, with three stories,

---

[1] *vineyards.* Up to our own times the remains of vines could be seen in the gardens of the old merchants' houses of Bermondsey.

[2] *platform.* Ground-plan.

one over another. The outsides of the walls be
made either of hard flint, or of plaster, or else of
brick, and the inner sides be well strengthened with
timber work. The roofs be plain and flat, covered
with a certain kind of plaster that is of no cost,
and yet so tempered that no fire can hurt or perish
it, and withstandeth the violence of the weather
better than any lead. They keep the wind out of their
windows with glass, for it is there much used, and
some here also with fine linen cloth dipped in oil
or amber, and that for two commodities. For by
this means more light cometh in, and the wind is
better kept out.

OF THE MAGISTRATES

EVERY thirty families or farms choose them yearly an officer, which in their old language is called the Syphogrant,[1] and by a newer name the Philarch. Every ten Syphogrants, with all their thirty families, be under an officer which was once called the Tranibor, now the chief Philarch. Moreover, as concerning the election of the prince,[2] all the Syphogrants, which be in number two hundred, first be sworn to choose him whom they think most meet and expedient. Then by a secret election, they name prince one of those four whom the people before named unto them. For out of the four quarters of the city there be four chosen, out of every quarter one, to stand for the election; which be put up to the council. The prince's office continueth all his lifetime, unless he be deposed or put down for suspicion of tyranny. They choose

---

[1] *Syphogrants and Tranibors.* The first word seems to be derived from συφεός, a sty, and the second from θρᾶνος, a bench, and βορός, devouring. Perhaps, as Dr. Lupton suggests, More, a member of Lincoln's Inn, is punning upon the names of the Benchers and Steward, bench-eaters and sty-ward.

[2] *election of the prince.* Robinson's use of the word ' prince ' must not make us think that there was a king of all Utopia. King Utopus seems to have had no successors. Utopia was a republic and the ' princes ' were but heads of the towns. We might call them ' mayors.'

the Tranibors yearly, but lightly they change them
not. All the other officers be but for one year.
The Tranibors every third day, and sometimes, if
need be, oftener, come into the council-house with
the prince. Their counsel is concerning the commonwealth. If there be any controversies among the
commoners, which be very few, they dispatch and
end them by and by. They take ever two Syphogrants to them in counsel, and every day a new
couple. And it is provided that nothing touching
the commonwealth shall be confirmed and ratified,
unless it have been reasoned of and debated three
days in the council before it be decreed.

It is death to have any consultation for the
commonwealth out of the council, or the place of
the common election. This statute, they say, was
made to the intent, that the prince and Tranibors
might not easily conspire together to oppress the
people by tyranny, and to change the state of the
weal public. Therefore matters of great weight
and importance be brought to the election-house of
the Syphogrants, which open the matter to their
families. And afterwards, when they have consulted
among themselves, they show their device to the
council. Sometimes the matter is brought before
the council of the whole island.

Furthermore, this custom also the council useth,
to dispute or reason of no matter the same day that
it is first proposed or put forth, but to defer it to
the next sitting of the council. Because that no
man when he hath rashly there spoken that cometh
to his tongue's end, shall then afterward rather
study for reasons wherewith to defend and maintain
his first foolish sentence, than for the commodity

of the commonwealth ; as one rather willing the
harm or hindrance of the weal public than any loss
or diminution of his own existimation. And as
one that would be ashamed (which is a very foolish
shame) to be counted anything at the first overseen
in the matter ; who at the first ought to have spoken
rather wisely, than hastily or rashly.

OF SCIENCES, CRAFTS, AND OCCUPATIONS

HUSBANDRY is a science common to them all in general, both men and women, wherein they be all expert and cunning. In this they be all instructed even from their youth; partly in their schools with traditions and precepts, and partly in the country nigh the city, brought up[1] as it were in playing, not only beholding the use of it, but by occasion of exercising their bodies practising it also.

Besides husbandry, which (as I said) is common to them all, every one of them learneth one or other several and particular science, as his own proper craft. That is most commonly either cloth-working in wool or flax, or masonry, of the smith's craft, or the carpenter's science. For there is none other occupation that any number to speak of doth use there. For their garments, which throughout all the island be of one fashion (saving that there is a difference between the man's garment and the woman's, between the married and the unmarried), and this one continueth for evermore unchanged, seemly and comely to the eye, no let to the moving and welding of the body, also fit both for winter and summer: as for these garments (I say) every

---

[1] *brought up.* The Latin *educti* means 'taken out,' i.e. into the fields, the work being treated as a recreation.

family maketh their own. But of the other foresaid
crafts every man learneth one. And not only the
men, but also the women. But the women, as the
weaker sort, be put to the easier crafts ; as to work
wool and flax. The more laboursome sciences be
committed to the men. For the most part every
man is brought up in his father's craft. For most
commonly they be naturally thereto bent and
inclined. But if a man's mind stand to any other,
he is by adoption put into a family of that occupation, which he doth most fantasy. Whom not only
his father, but also the magistrates do diligently
look to, that he be put to a discreet and an honest
householder. Yea, and if any person, when he hath
learned one craft, be desirous to learn also another,
he is likewise suffered and permitted.

When he hath learned both, he occupieth whether
he will ; unless the city have more need of the one
than of the other. The chief and almost the only
office of the Syphogrants is, to see and take heed
that no man sit idle, but that every one apply his
own craft with earnest diligence ; and yet for all
that, not to be wearied, from early in the morning
to late in the evening, with continual work, like
labouring and toiling beasts. For this is worse
than the miserable and wretched condition of
bondmen, which nevertheless is almost everywhere
the life of workmen and artificers, saving in
Utopia.

For they, dividing the day and the night into
twenty-four just hours, appoint and assign only
six of those hours to work ;[1] three before noon,

---

[1] *toiling beasts.* Dr. Lupton quotes an act passed in 1495
and revived in 1514 which fixed the hours of work for

upon the which they go straight to dinner; and after dinner, when they have rested two hours, then they work three hours, and upon that they go to supper. About eight of the clock in the evening (counting one of the clock at the first hour after noon) they go to bed; eight hours they give to sleep. All the void time, that is between the hours of work, sleep, and meat, that they be suffered to bestow, every man as he liketh best himself. Not to the intent that they should misspend this time in riot or slothfulness;[1] but being then licensed from the labour of their own occupations, to bestow the time well and thriftily upon some other science, as shall please them. For it is a solemn custom there to have lectures daily early in the morning; where to be present they only be constrained that be namely chosen and appointed to learning. Howbeit a great multitude of every sort of people, both men and women, go to hear lectures, some one and some another, as every man's nature is inclined. Yet, this notwithstanding, if any man had rather bestow this time upon his own occupation (as it chanceth in many, whose minds rise not in the contemplation of any science liberal) he is not letted nor prohibited, but is also praised and commended, as profitable to the commonwealth.

artificers and labourers. From September to March they were all the hours of daylight: from March to September from before 5 a.m. to 7 or 8 p.m., with two intervals for meals.

[1] *slothfulness*. In conformity with this, More 'would never allow (his servants) to waste their time in sloth and improper pastimes . . . dice or cards.' (Stapleton, p. 95.) Music, on the other hand, was encouraged.

K

After supper they bestow one hour in play ; in summer in their gardens, in winter in their common halls where they dine and sup. There they exercise themselves in music, or else in honest and wholesome communication. Dice-play, and such other foolish and pernicious games they know not. But they use two games not much unlike the chess. The one is the battle of numbers, wherein one number stealeth away another. The other is wherein vices fight with virtues, as it were in battle array, or a set field. In the which game is very properly showed both the strife and discord that vices have among themselves, and again their unity and concord against virtues ; and also what vices be repugnant to what virtues : with what power and strength they assail them openly ; by what wiles and subtlety they assault them secretly : with what help and aid the virtues resist, and overcome the puissance of the vices ; by what craft they frustrate their purposes : and finally by what sleight or means the one getteth the victory.

But here lest you be deceived, one thing you must look more narrowly upon. For seeing they bestow but six hours in work, perchance you may think that the lack of some necessary things hereof may ensue. But this is nothing so. For that small time is not only enough, but also too much for the store and abundance of all things that be requisite, either for the necessity or commodity of life. The which thing you also shall perceive, if you weigh and consider with yourselves how great a part of the people in other countries liveth idle. First, almost all women, which be the half of the whole number ; or else if the women be somewhere occupied, there most commonly in their stead the men be idle. Besides this, how great and how idle a company is there of priests and religious men, as they call them ?[1] Put thereto all rich men, specially all landed men, which commonly be called gentlemen, and noblemen. Take into this number also their servants : I mean all that flock of stout bragging rush-bucklers.[2] Joined to them also sturdy and valiant beggars, cloaking their idle life under the colour of some disease or sickness. And truly you shall find them much fewer than you thought, by whose labour all these things are wrought, that in men's affairs are now daily used and frequented. Now consider with yourself, of those few that do work, how few be occupied in necessary works. For where money beareth all the swing, there many vain and superfluous occupations must needs be used, to serve only for riotous superfluity and unhonest pleasure. For the same multitude that now is occupied in work, if they were divided into so few occupations as the necessary use of nature requireth ; in so great plenty of things as then of necessity would ensue, doubtless the prices would be too little for the artificers to maintain their livings. But if all these that be now busied about unprofitable occupations,

[1] *priests and religious men, as they call them.* One of the hoariest of jokes among Catholics is based on the twofold meaning of ' religious '—on the one hand ' pious,' and on the other ' one who has taken public vows in a society approved by the Church,' e.g. a Benedictine or a Franciscan. It was More's loyalty to the Church that led him to maintain that too many subjects were admitted to ordination. See below, note on p. 208.

[2] *rush-bucklers.* Swashbucklers.

with all the whole flock of them that live idly and slothfully, which consume and waste every one of them more of these things that come by other men's labour, than two of the workmen themselves do : if all these (I say) were set to profitable occupations, you easily perceive how little time would be enough, yea and too much, to store us with all things that many be requisite either for necessity or for commodity, yea or for pleasure, so that the same pleasure be true and natural.

And this in Utopia the thing itself maketh manifest and plain. For there in all the city, with the whole country or shire adjoining to it, scarcely five hundred persons of all the whole number of men and women, that be neither too old nor too weak to work, be licensed and discharged from labour. Among them be the Syphogrants (who though they be by the laws exempt and privileged from labour) yet they exempt not themselves ; to the intent that they may the rather by their example provoke others to work. The same vacation from labour do they also enjoy to whom the people, persuaded by the commendation of the priests and secret election of the Syphogrants, have given a perpetual licence from labour to learning. But if any one of them prove not according to the expectation and hope of him conceived, he is forthwith plucked back to the company of artificers. And contrariwise, often it chanceth that a handi-craftsman doth so earnestly bestow his vacant and spare hours in learning, and through diligence so profiteth therein, that he is taken from his handy occupation, and promoted to the company of the learned. Out of this order of the learned be chosen

ambassadors, priests, Tranibors, and finally the
prince himself. Whom they in their old tongue
call Barzanes,[1] and by a newer name, Ademus.[2]
The residue of the people being neither idle, nor
yet occupied about unprofitable exercises, it may
be easily judged in how few hours how much good
work by them may be done and dispatched, towards
those things that I have spoken of.

This commodity they have also above others,
that in the most part of necessary occupations
they need not so much work as other nations do.
For first of all the building or repairing of houses
asketh everywhere so many men's continual labour,
because that the unthrifty heir suffereth the houses
that his father built in continuance of time to fall
in decay. So that which he might have upholden
with little cost, his successor is constrained to
build it again anew, to his great charge. Yea,
many times also the house that stood one man in
much money, another is of so nice and so delicate
a mind that he setteth nothing by it. And it being
neglected, and therefore shortly falling into ruin,
he buildeth up another in another place with no
less cost and charge. But among the Utopians,
where all things be set in a good order, and the
commonwealth in a good stay, it very seldom
chanceth that they choose a new plot to build a
house upon. And they do not only find speedy
and quick remedies for present faults, but also

[1] *Barzanes.* A Persian name. More will say later on
(p. 159) that the Utopian speech ' is not much unlike the
Persian tongue.'

[2] *Ademus.* From ἀ-, ' not ' or ' without,' and δῆμος, ' a
people.'

prevent them that be like to fall. And by this means their houses continue and last very long with little labour and small reparations; in so much that this kind of workmen sometimes have almost nothing to do. But that they be commanded to hew timber at home, and to square and trim up stones, to the intent that if any work chance, it may the speedier rise.

Now, sir, in their apparel, mark (I pray you) how few workmen they need. First of all, whilst they be at work, they be covered homely with leather or skins, that will last seven years. When they go forth abroad they cast upon them a cloak,[1] which hideth the other homely apparel. These cloaks throughout the whole island be all of one colour, and that is the natural colour of the wool. They therefore do not only spend much less woollen cloth than is spent in other countries, but also the same standeth them in much less cost. But linen cloth is made with less labour, and is therefore had more in use. But in linen cloth only whiteness, in woollen only cleanliness, is regarded. As for the smallness or fineness of the thread, that is nothing passed for. And this is the cause wherefor in other places four or five cloth gowns of divers colours, and as many silk coats, be not enough for one man. Yea, and if he be of the delicate and nice sort, ten be too few; whereas there one garment will serve a man most commonly two years. For why should he desire more? Seeing if he had them, he should not be the better happed or covered from cold, neither in his apparel any whit the comelier.

[1] *cloak*. In a letter to Erasmus More speaks of this as a Franciscan cloak. (Allen, II, 499.)

Wherefore, seeing they be all exercised in profitable occupations, and that few artificers in the same crafts be sufficient, this is the cause that, plenty of all things being among them, they do sometimes bring forth an innumerable company of people to amend the highways, if any be broken. Many times also, when they have no such work to be occupied about, an open proclamation is made, that they shall bestow fewer hours in work. For the magistrates do not exercise their citizens against their wills in unneedful labours. For why, in the institution of that weal public, this end is only and chiefly pretended and minded, that what time may possibly be spared from the necessary occupations and affairs of the commonwealth, all that the citizens should withdraw from the bodily service to the free liberty of the mind and garnishing of the same. For herein they suppose the felicity of this life to consist.

OF THEIR LIVING AND MUTUAL
CONVERSATION TOGETHER

BUT now will I declare how the citizens use
themselves one towards another; what familiar
occupying and entertainment there is among the
people, and what fashion they use in the distribution
of everything. First the city consisteth of families,[1]
the families most commonly be made of kindreds.
For the women, when they be married at a lawful
age, they go into their husbands' houses. But the
male children, with all the whole male offspring,
continue still in their own family and be governed
of the eldest and ancientest father, unless he dote
for age; for then the next to him in age is placed
in his room.

But to the intent the prescript number of the
citizens should neither decrease nor above measure
increase, it is ordained that no family, which in
every city be six thousand in the whole, besides
them of the country, shall at once have fewer
children of the age of fourteen years or thereabout

---

[1] *families.* Not in the limited modern sense, but a household like More's own, where, however, not only the boy,
but the girls also, continued to reside with their father after
their marriage; where too other 'children of the age of
fourteen years or thereabouts' (which is Robinson's in-
accurate expansion of the *puberes*, i.e. adults, of the original)
were admitted, like Margaret Gigs and John Clement, her
future husband.

than ten or more than sixteen, for of children under this age no number can be prescribed or appointed. This measure or number is easily observed and kept, by putting them that in fuller families be above the number into families of smaller increase. But if chance be that in the whole city the store increase above the just number, therewith they fill up the lack of other cities.

But if so be that the multitude throughout the whole island pass and exceed the due number, then they choose out of every city certain citizens, and build up a town under their own laws in the next land where the inhabitants have much waste and unoccupied ground,[1] receiving also of the same country people to them, if they will join and dwell with them. They thus joining and dwelling together do easily agree in one fashion of living, and that to the great wealth of both the peoples. For they so bring the matter about by their laws, that the ground which before was neither good nor profitable for the one nor for the other, is now sufficient and fruitful enough for them both. But if the inhabitants of that land will not dwell with them to be ordered by their laws, then they drive them out of those bounds which they have limited and appointed out for themselves. And if they resist and rebel, then they make war against

[1] *waste and unoccupied ground*. The right to colonise such land may well have been a topic of conversation in More's family, for in March, 1517, a few months after the first edition of *Utopia*, his brother-in-law, John Rastell, sank a lot of money in an expedition to Newfoundland. Rastell's ship got no farther than Waterford where his rebellious crew put him on shore and left him. (See *Early Tudor Drama*, by Professor A. W. Reed, p. 11.)

them. For they count this the most just cause of
war, when any people holdeth a piece of ground
void and vacant to no good nor profitable use,
keeping others from the use and possession of it,
which notwithstanding by the law of nature ought
thereof to be nourished and relieved. If any chance
do so much diminish the number of any of their
cities that it cannot be filled up again, without the
diminishing of the just number of the other cities
(which they say chanced but twice since the beginning of the land through a great pestilent plague),
then they fulfil and make up the number with
citizens fetched out of their own foreign towns,
for they had rather suffer their foreign towns to
decay and perish, than any city of their own island
to be diminished.

But now again to the conversation of the citizens
among themselves. The eldest (as I said) ruleth
the family. The wives be ministers to their
husbands, the children to their parents, and, to be
short, the younger to their elders. Every city is
divided into four equal parts or quarters. In the
midst of every quarter there is a market-place of
all manner of things. Thither the works of every
family be brought into certain houses. And every
kind of thing is laid up several in barns or storehouses. From thence the father of every family,
or every householder, fetcheth whatsoever he and
his hath need of, and carrieth it away with him
without money, without exchange, without any
gage, pawn, or pledge. For why should anything
be denied unto him? Seeing there is abundance
of all things, and that it is not to be feared lest
any man will ask more than he needeth. For why

should it be thought that that man would ask
more than enough which is sure never to lack ?
Certainly in all kinds of living creatures either fear
of lack doth cause covetousness and raven, or in
man only pride, which counteth it a glorious thing
to pass and excel others in the superfluous and vain
ostentation of things. The which kind of vice
among the Utopians can have no place.

Next to the market-places that I spake of, stand
meat markets ; whither be brought not only all
sorts of herbs, and the fruits of trees, with bread,
but also fish, and all manner of four-footed beasts
and wild-fowl that be man's meat. But first the
filthiness and odour thereof is clean washed away
in the running river without the city, in places
appointed meet for the same purpose. From thence
the beasts be brought in killed, and clean washed
by the hands of their bondmen. For they permit
not their free citizens to accustom themselves to
the killing of beasts, through the use whereof they
think clemency, the gentlest affection of our nature,
by little and little to decay and perish. Neither they
suffer anything that is filthy, loathsome, or un-
cleanly, to be brought into the city, lest the air by
the stench thereof, infected and corrupt, should
cause pestilent diseases.

Moreover, every street hath certain great large
halls set in equal distance one from another, every
one known by a several name. In these halls dwell
the Syphogrants. And to every one of the same
halls be appointed thirty families, on either side
fifteen. The stewards of every hall at a certain hour
come in to the meat markets, where they receive
meat according to the number of their halls.

But first, and chiefly of all, respect is had to the sick, that be cured in the hospitals. For in the circuit of the city, a little without the walls, they have four hospitals,[1] so big, so wide, so ample, and so large, that they may seem four little towns, which were devised of that bigness partly to the intent the sick, be they never so many in number, should not lie too throng or strait, and, therefore, uneasily and incommodiously; and partly that they which were taken and holden with contagious diseases, such as be wont by infection to creep from one to another, might be laid apart far from the company of the residue. These hospitals be so well appointed, and with all things necessary to health so furnished, and, moreover, so diligent attendance through the continual presence of cunning physicians is given, that though no man be sent thither against his will, yet, notwithstanding, there is no sick person in all the city that had not rather lie there than at home in his own house.

When the steward of the sick hath received such meats as the physicians have prescribed, then the best is equally divided among the halls, according

---

[1] *Four hospitals.* There were four great hospitals for the sick in pre-Reformation London, not one only, as Dr. Lupton, followed by Churton Collins, supposes. All four were confiscated by Henry VIII. Public opinion forced him to restore one on his deathbed, St. Bartholomew's, of which he is now ironically called 'the second founder.' Another, St. Thomas's, was bought back at full price by the city from Edward VI; the others were forever destroyed, and yet one of them, St. Mary's, outside Bishopsgate, was larger than either St. Thomas's or 'Bart's.' The fourth was Elsing Spital, which had an income of about £200 per annum. See Chambers, p. 260.

to the company of every one, saving that there is had a respect to the prince, the bishop,[1] the Tranibors, and to ambassadors, and all strangers, if there be any, which be very few and seldom. But they also, when they be there, have certain several houses appointed and prepared for them.

To these halls at the set hours of dinner and supper cometh all the whole Syphogranty or ward, warned by the noise of a brazen trumpet ; except such as be sick in the hospitals, or else in their own houses. Howbeit no man is prohibited or forbid, after the halls be served, to fetch home meat out of the market to his own house, for they know that no man will do it without a cause reasonable. For though no man be prohibited to dine at home, yet no man doth it willingly, because it is counted a point of small honesty. And also it were a folly to take the pain to dress a bad dinner at home, when they may be welcome to good and fine fare so nigh hand at the hall. In this hall all vile service, all slavery and drudgery, with all laboursome toil and base business, is done by bondmen. But the women of every family by course have the office and charge of cookery for setting and dressing the meat, and ordering all things thereto belonging. They sit at three tables or more, according to the number of their company. The men sit upon the bench next the wall, and the women against them on the other side of the table, that if any sudden evil should chance to them as many times happeneth to women with child, they may rise without trouble or disturbance of anybody, and go thence into the nursery.

[1] *bishop.* See below, note on p. 208.

The nurses sit several along with their young
sucklings in a certain parlour appointed and deputed
to the same purpose, never without fire and clean
water, nor yet without cradles, that when they
will they may lay down the young infants, and at
their pleasure take them out of their swathing
clothes, and hold them to the fire, and refresh
them with play. Every mother is nurse to her own
child, unless either death or sickness be the let.
When that chanceth, the wives of the Syphogrants
quickly provide a nurse. And that is not hard to
be done. For they that can do it, prefer themselves
to no service so gladly as to that. Because that
there this kind of pity is much praised : and the
child that is nourished, ever after taketh his nurse
for his own natural mother. Also among the
nurses sit all the children that be under the age of
five years. All the other children of both kinds, as
well boys as girls, that be under the age of marriage,
do either serve at the tables, or else if they be too
young thereto, yet they stand by with marvellous
silence. That which is given to them from the
table they eat, and other several dinner-time they
have none.

The Syphogrant and his wife sit in the midst
of the high table, forasmuch as that is counted the
honourablest place, and because from thence all
the whole company is in their sight. For that table
standeth overthwart the over end of the hall. To
them be joined two of the ancientest and eldest.
For at every table they sit four at a mess. But if
there be a church standing in that Syphogranty or
ward, then the priest and his wife[1] sitteth with the
Syphogrant as chief in the company. On both

---

[1] *wife*. See below, note on p. 211.

sides of them sit young men, and next unto them
again old men. And thus throughout all the house
equal of age be set together, and yet be mixed
and matched with unequal ages. This, they say,
was ordained, to the intent that the sage gravity
and reverence of the elders should keep the youngers
from wanton licence of words and behaviour.
Forasmuch as nothing can be so secretly spoken
or done at the table, but either they that sit on the
one side or on the other must needs perceive it.
The dishes be not set down in order from the
first place, but all the old men (whose places be
marked with some special token to be known) be
first served of their meat, and then the residue
equally. The old men divide their dainties[1] as they
think best to the younger on each side of them.
Thus the elders be not defrauded of their due
honour, and, nevertheless, equal commodity cometh
to every one.

They begin every dinner and supper of reading[2]
something that pertaineth to good manners and
virtue. But it is short, because no man shall be
grieved therewith. Hereof the elders take occasion
of honest communication, but neither sad nor
unpleasant. Howbeit they do not spend all the
whole dinner-time themselves with long and
tedious talks, but they gladly hear also the young
men ; yea, and purposely provoke them to talk,

[1] *dainties*. Robinson omits to translate a few words—
' of which there is not a quantity sufficient to be served
round to all.'

[2] *reading*. The Latin marginal note states that at present
this monastic custom was not strictly observed. But More
observed it in his own house (Stapleton, p. 97) where it was
followed by conversation, as here.

to the intent that they may have a proof of every man's wit, and towardness or disposition to virtue, which commonly in the liberty of feasting doth show and utter itself. Their dinners be very short; but their suppers be somewhat longer; because that after dinner followeth labour, after supper sleep and natural rest, which they think to be of more strength and efficacy to wholesome and healthful digestion. No supper is passed without music. Nor their banquets lack no conceits nor junkets. They burn sweet gums and spices for perfumes and pleasant smells, and sprinkle about sweet ointments and waters, yea, they leave nothing undone that maketh for the cheering of the company. For they be much inclined to this opinion : to think no kind of pleasure forbidden,[1] whereof cometh no harm.

Thus, therefore, and after this sort they live together in the city, but in the country they that dwell alone far from any neighbours, do dine and sup at home in their own houses. For no family there lacketh any kind of victuals, as from whom cometh all that the citizens eat and live by.

[1] *no pleasure forbidden*. See below, note on p. 145.

OF THEIR JOURNEYING OR
TRAVELLING ABROAD

*With divers other matters cunningly reasoned
and wittily discussed*

BUT if any be desirous to visit either their
friends dwelling in another city, or to see the
place itself, they easily obtain licence of their
Syphogrants and Tranibors, unless there be some
profitable let.[1] No man goeth out alone, but a
company is sent forth together with their prince's
letters, which do testify that they have licence to
go that journey, and prescribeth also the day of their
return. They have a wagon given them, with a
common bondman, which driveth the oxen and
taketh charge of them. But unless they have women
in their company, they send home the wagon again,
as an impediment and a let. And though they
carry nothing forth with them, yet in all their
journey they lack nothing. For wheresoever they
come, they be at home. If they tarry in a place
longer than one day, then there every one of them
falleth to his own occupation,[2] and be very gently

[1] *some profitable let.* Some business at home to detain
them.

[2] *his own occupation.* Perhaps More thought of St. Paul
who, coming to Corinth, found a Jew, Aquila, and his wife
Priscilla, ' and because he was of the same trade, he remained
with them and wrought. Now they were tent-makers by
trade.' (*Acts* xviii, 3.)

entertained of the workmen and companies of the same crafts. If any man of his own head, and without leave, walk out of his precinct and bounds, taken without the prince's letters, he is brought again for a fugitive or a runaway with great shame and rebuke, and is sharply punished. If he be taken in that fault again, he is punished with bondage.

If any be desirous to walk abroad into the fields, or into the country that belongeth to the same city that he dwelleth in, obtaining the goodwill of his father and the consent of his wife, he is not prohibited. But into what part of the country soever he cometh he hath no meat given him until he hath wrought out his forenoon's task, or dispatched so much work as there is wont to be wrought before supper. Observing this law and condition, he may go whither he will within the bounds of his own city. For he shall be no less profitable to the city than if he were within it.

Now you see how little liberty they have to loiter : how they can have no cloak or pretence to idleness. There be neither wine-taverns, nor ale-houses, nor stews, nor any occasion of vice or wickedness, no lurking corners, no places of wicked counsels or unlawful assemblies. But they be in the present sight, and under the eyes of every man. So that of necessity they must either apply their accustomed labours, or else recreate themselves with honest and laudable pastimes.

This fashion and trade of life, being used among the people, it cannot be chosen, but that they must of necessity have store and plenty of all things. And seeing they be all thereof partners equally, therefore can no man there be poor or needy. In

the council of Amaurote, whither, as I said, every
city sendeth three men apiece yearly, as soon as it
is perfectly known of what things there is in every
place plenty, and, again, what things be scant in
any place; incontinent the lack of the one is
performed and filled up with the abundance of
the other. And this they do freely without any
benefit, taking nothing again of them to whom
the things is given, but those cities that have given
of their store to any other city that lacketh, requiring
nothing again of the same city, do take such things
as they lack of another city, to the which they gave
nothing. So the whole island is, as it were, one
family or household.

But when they have made sufficient provision of
store for themselves (which they think not done,
until they have provided for two years following,
because of the uncertainty of the next year's proof),
then of those things whereof they have abundance
they carry forth into other countries great plenty :
as grain, honey, wool, flax, wood, madder, purple-
dyed fells, wax, tallow, leather, and living beasts.
And the seventh part of all these things they give
frankly and freely to the poor of that country. The
residue they sell at a reasonable and mean price.

By this trade of traffic or merchandise, they bring
into their own country, not only great plenty of
gold and silver, but also all such things as they lack
at home, which is almost nothing but iron. And
by reason they have long used this trade, now they
have more abundance of these things than any
man will believe. Now, therefore, they care not
whether they sell for ready money, or else upon
trust to be paid at a day, and to have the most part

in debts. But in so doing they never follow the credence of private men, but the assurance or warranty of the whole city, by instruments and writings made in that behalf accordingly. When the day of payment is come and expired, the city gathereth up the debt of the private debtors, and putteth it into the common box, and so long hath the use and profit of it, until the Utopians their creditors demand it. The most part of it they never ask. For that thing which is to them no profit, to take it from others to whom it is profitable they think it no right nor conscience.

But if the case so stand, that they must lend part of that money to another people, then they require their debt; or when they have war. For the which purpose only they keep at home all the treasure which they have, to be helped and secured by it either in extreme jeopardies or in sudden dangers, but especially and chiefly to hire therewith, and that for unreasonable great wages, strange soldiers. For they had rather put strangers in jeopardy than their own countrymen; knowing that for money enough, their enemies themselves many times may be bought or sold, or else through treason be set together by the ears among themselves. For this cause they keep an inestimable treasure. But yet not as a treasure; but so they have it, and use it, as in good faith I am ashamed to show, fearing that my words shall not be believed. And this I have more cause to fear, for that I know how difficultly and hardly I myself would have believed another man telling the same, if I had not presently seen it with mine own eyes. For it must needs be, that how far a thing is dissonant and disagreeing from the guise and trade of the hearers, so far shall it be out of their belief. Howbeit, a wise and indifferent esteemer of things will not greatly marvel perchance, seeing all their other laws and customs do so much differ from ours, if the use also of gold and silver among them be applied rather to their own fashions than to ours. I mean in that they occupy not money themselves, but keep it for that chance, which as it may happen, so it may be that it shall never come to pass.

In the meantime gold and silver,[1] whereof money is made, they do so use, as none of them doth more esteem it than the very nature of the thing deserveth. And then who doth not plainly see how far it is under iron, as without the which men can no better live than without fire and water. Whereas to gold and silver nature hath given no use that we may not well lack, if that the folly of men had not set it in higher estimation for the rareness' sake. But of the contrary part, nature as a most tender and loving mother, hath placed the best and most necessary things open abroad; as the air, the water, and the earth itself; and hath removed and hid farthest from us vain and unprofitable things. Therefore if these metals among them should be fast locked up in some tower, it might be suspected that the prince and the council (as the people is

[1] *gold and silver.* Plato would not allow his 'guardians' to touch gold and silver (*Republic*, Book III, p. 245), but More's humorous elaboration of the superior usefulness of iron is all his own. He returns to the same point in his *Dialogue of Comfort*, p. 195. He had read in *Ecclesiasticus*, xxxix, 31, 'The principal things necessary for the life of man are water, fire and iron, salt, milk, and bread of flour, and honey, and the cluster of the grape, and oil and clothing.'

ever foolishly imagining) intended by some subtlety
to deceive the commons, and to take some profit
of it to themselves. Furthermore if they should
make thereof plate and such other finely and
cunningly wrought stuff, if at any time they should
have occasion to break it and melt it again, therewith to pay their soldiers' wages, they see and
perceive very well that men would be loath to
part from those things that they once began to
have pleasure and delight in.

To remedy all this they have found out a means,
which, as it is agreeable to all their other laws and
customs, so it is from ours, where gold is so much
set by, and so diligently kept, very far discrepant
and repugnant ; and therefore incredible, but only
to them that be wise.[1] For whereas they eat and
drink in earthen and glass vessels, which indeed be
curiously and properly made, and yet be of very
small value, of gold and silver they make commonly
chamber-pots, and other vessels that serve for most
vile uses, not only in their common halls, but in
every man's private house. Furthermore of the
same metals they make great chains, fetters, and
gyves wherein they tie their bondmen. Finally,
whosoever for any offence be infamed, by their
ears hang rings of gold ; upon their fingers they
wear rings of gold, and about their necks chains of
gold ;[2] and in conclusion their heads be tied about

[1] *to them that be wise.* The Latin is simply *peritis*, i.e. ' to
those who have seen the custom.'

[2] *chains of gold.* ' It is amusing,' writes Father Bridgett
(p. 184), ' that the writer of all this should have been made
a knight, or as he was then called, *Eques auratus*, ' a gilded
knight,' because this dignity both entitled him and required
of him to wear golden insignia, and to deck with gold the

with gold. Thus by all means possible they procure
to have gold and silver among them in reproach
and infamy. And these metals, which other nations
do as grievously and sorrowfully forego, as in a
manner their own lives, if they should altogether
at once be taken from the Utopians, no man there
would think that he had lost the worth of one
farthing.

They gather also pearls by the seaside, and
diamonds and carbuncles upon certain rocks ; and
yet they seek not for them, but by chance finding
them, they cut and polish them. And therewith
they deck their young infants. Which like as in
the first years of their childhood, they make much
and be fond and proud of such ornaments, so when
they be a little more grown in years and discretion,
perceiving that none but children do wear such
toys and trifles, they lay them away even of their
own shamefastness, without any bidding of their
parents : even as our children, when they wax big,
do cast away nuts, brooches, and puppets. Therefore these laws and customs, which be so far
different from all other nations, how diverse
fantasies also and minds they do cause, did I
never so plainly perceive, as in the ambassadors of
the Anemolians.[1]

trappings of his horse (Selden's *Titles of Honour*, p. 437), and
that he should generally be represented as wearing round his
neck one of those massive gold chains, which he made the
badge of notorious malefactors among his Utopians.' The
year before he was knighted he had to attend, with his
royal master, a function for which he had an equal distaste,
the Field of the Cloth of Gold.

  [1] *Anemolians*. From ἄνεμος, the wind, and thus ' empty,
vain.'

These ambassadors came to Amaurote while I was there. And because they came to entreat of great and weighty matters, those three citizens apiece out of every city were come thither before them. But all the ambassadors of the next countries, which had been there before, and knew the fashions and manners of the Utopians, among whom they perceived no honour given to sumptuous apparel, silks to be contemned, gold also to be infamed and reproachful, were wont to come thither in very homely and simple array. But the Anemolians, because they dwell far thence and had very little acquaintance with them, hearing that they were all apparelled alike, and that very rudely and homely; thinking them not to have the things which they did not wear; being, therefore, more proud than wise; determined in the gorgeousness of their apparel to represent very gods, and with the bright shining and glistering of their gay clothing to dazzle the eyes of the silly[1] poor Utopians. So there came in three ambassadors with a hundred servants all apparelled in changeable colours; the most of them in silks, the ambassadors themselves (for at home in their own country they were noble men) in cloth of gold, with great chains of gold, with gold hanging at their ears, with gold rings upon their fingers, with brooches and aglets of gold upon their caps, which glistered full of pearls and precious stones: to be short, trimmed and adorned with all those things, which among the Utopians were either the punishment of bondmen, of the reproach of infamed persons, or else trifles for young children to play withal. Therefore it

[1] *silly*. Pitiable, miserable.

would have done a man good at his heart to have seen how proudly they displayed their peacocks' feathers, how much they made of their painted sheaths, and how lofty they set forth and advanced themselves, when they compared their gallant apparel with the poor raiment of the Utopians. For all the people were swarmed forth into the streets. And on the other side it was no less pleasure to consider how much they were deceived, and how far they missed of their purpose, being contrariwise taken than they thought they should have been. For to the eyes of all the Utopians, except very few, which had been in other countries for some reasonable cause, all that gorgeousness of apparel seemed shameful and reproachful. Insomuch that they most reverently saluted the vilest and most abject of them for lords : passing over the ambassadors themselves without any honour : judging them by their wearing of golden chains to be bondmen. Yea, you should have seen children also, that had cast away their pearls and precious stones, when they saw the like sticking upon the ambassadors' caps, dig and push their mothers under the sides, saying thus to them : ' Look, mother, how great a lubber doth yet wear pearls and precious stones, as though he were a little child still.' But the mother, yea and that also in good earnest : ' Peace, son,' saith she : ' I think he be some of the ambassadors' fools.' Some found fault at their golden chains, as to no use nor purpose, being so small and weak that a bondman might easily break them, and again so wide and large that when it pleased him he might cast them off, and run away at liberty whither he would.

But when the ambassadors had been there a day
or two and saw so great abundance of gold so
lightly esteemed, yea, in no less reproach than it
was with them in honour; and besides that more
gold in the chains and gyves of one fugitive bondman
than all the costly ornaments of them three were
worth; they began to abate their courage, and for
very shame laid away all that gorgeous array whereof
they were so proud, and especially when they had
talked familiarly with the Utopians, and had learned
all their fashions and opinions. For they marvel
that any men be so foolish as to have delight and
pleasure in the doubtful glistering of a little trifling
stone, which may behold any of the stars, or else
the sun itself. Or that any man is so mad as to
count himself the nobler for the smaller or finer
thread of wool, which selfsame wool (be it now in
never so fine a spun thread) a sheep did once wear;
and yet was she all that time no other thing than a
sheep.

They marvel also that gold, which of the own
nature is a thing so unprofitable, is now among all
people in so high estimation, that man himself, by
whom, yea, and for the use of whom, it is so much
set by, is in much less estimation than the gold
itself. Insomuch that a lumpish, block-headed
churl, and which hath no more wit than an ass,
yea, and as full of naughtiness as of folly, shall have
nevertheless many wise and good men in subjection
and bondage, only for this, because he hath a great
heap of gold. Which if it should be taken from
him by any fortune, or by some subtle wile and
cautel of the law (which no less than fortune
doth both raise up the low and pluck down the

high), and be given to the most vile slave and
abject drivel of all his household, then shortly after
he shall go into the service of his servant as an
augmentation or overplus beside his money. But
they much more marvel at and detest the madness
of them, which to those rich men, in whose debt
and danger they be not, do give almost divine
honours, for none other consideration but because
they be rich ; and yet knowing them to be such
niggardish penny-fathers, that they be sure as long
as they live, not the worth of one farthing of that
heap of gold shall come to them.

These and suchlike opinions have they conceived,
partly by education, being brought up in that
commonwealth whose laws and customs be far
different from these kinds of folly, and partly by
good literature and learning. For though there be
not many in every city which be exempt and
discharged of all other labours, and appointed only
to learning, that is to say, such in whom even
from their very childhood they have perceived a
singular towardness, a fine wit, and a mind apt to
good learning ; yet all in their childhood[1] be
instructed in learning. And the better part of the
people, both men and women, throughout all their
whole life do bestow on learning those spare hours
which we said they have vacant from bodily
labours. They be taught learning in their own native
tongue. For it is both copious in words,[2] and also

---

[1] *all in their childhood.* England had to wait until 1870
for even the beginnings of universal education.

[2] *copious in words.* Dr. Lupton's suggestion that More
may here be thinking of our English tongue, to the enrichment and development of which he made such important

pleasant to the ear ; and for the utterance of a man's mind very perfect and sure. The most part of all that side of the world useth the same language, saving that among the Utopians it is finest and purest, and according to the diversity of the countries it is diversely altered.

Of all these philosophers whose names be here famous in this part of the world to us known, before our coming thither not as much as the fame of any of them was come among them. And yet in music, logic, arithmetic, and geometry[1] they have found out in a manner all that our ancient philosophers have taught. But as they in all things be almost equal to our old ancient clerks, so our new logicians in subtle inventions have far passed and gone beyond them. For they have not devised one of all those rules of restrictions, amplifications, and suppositions,[2] very wittily invented in the small

contributions, may perhaps find support in a passage of his Dialogue. ' For as for that our tongue is called barbarous, is but a fantasy ; for so is, as every learned man knoweth, every strange tongue to other. And if they would call it barren of words, there is no doubt but it is plenteous enough to express our minds in anything whereof one man hath used to speak with another.' (E. W., p. 243.)

[1] *Music, Logic, Arithmetic, and Geometry.* Forming, with Grammar, Rhetoric, and Astronomy, the seven liberal arts which, divided into the *trivium* and the *quadrivium*, were the basis of ancient education.

[2] *restrictions, amplifications, suppositions.* The explanation of these and other terms is found in the last treatise (headed *Parva Logicalia,* ' Small Logicals ') of the *Summulae Logicales,* a work issued in 1250 by Peter of Spain, the future Pope John XXI. It was the most original work on logic since the time of Aristotle and first contained the famous lines, *Barbara, Celarent,* etc. William of Occam (died 1349) accepted

logicals, which here our children in every place do learn. Furthermore they were never yet able to find out the second intentions ; insomuch that none of them all could ever see man himself in common,[1] as they call him, though he be (as you know) bigger than ever was any giant, yea, and pointed to of us even with our finger.

and improved the work of Peter of Spain, but his followers, the Nominalists of the fourteenth and fifteenth centuries, by their excessive subtleties brought the noble science of logic into a disrepute from which it has hardly yet recovered. (See *Catholic Encyclopedia*, art. Logic, esp. p. 327, col. 1.)

[1] *man in common.* In the age-long discussion of what degree of reality is to be ascribed to a universal idea, e.g. man in the abstract, Plato adopted a position of extreme realism, but some of his later followers, especially the School of Chartres in the eleventh and twelfth centuries, took a still more exaggerated view, and fully deserved More's sarcasm.

The distinction between first and second intentions may be thus illustrated. If I say ' I see a man ' I express the knowledge derived from my sense of sight. This is knowledge of the first intention, for it is always the first act or ' intention ' of the mind to represent things without reference to other things or ideas. But if now I reflect upon this first intention or notion of ' man ' as it is in my mind, I can lay down many propositions with regard to it, e.g. that it is a nature common to many, that it can be considered as a subject or a predicate, a species or a genus, etc. These latter are called ' second intentions ' because they are ideas acquired not when the intellect first apprehends the thing, but afterwards when it reflects on its first knowledge of the thing and viewing it mentally forms additional conceptions of it. The process is described by St. Thomas Aquinas. In I Sent., dist. 2, q. 1, a. 3.

Whether the terms first and second intentions be used or not, the distinction itself, it will thus be seen, is absolutely essential to logical reasoning. Not even in Utopia would logic (see a few lines earlier in the text) be possible without it.

But they be in the course of the stars and the movings of the heavenly spheres very expert and cunning. They have also wittily excogitated and devised instruments of divers fashions, wherein is exactly comprehended and contained the movings and situations of the sun, the moon, and of all the other stars, which appear in their horizon. But as for the amities and dissensions of the planets, and all that deceitful divination[1] by the stars, they never as much as dreamed thereof. Rains, winds, and other courses of tempests they know before by certain tokens, which they have learned by long use and observation. But of the causes of all these things, and of the ebbing, flowing, and saltness of the sea, and, finally, of the original beginning and nature of heaven and of the world, they hold partly the same opinions that our old philosophers hold, and partly, as our philosophers vary among themselves, so they also, while they bring new reasons of things, do disagree from all them, and yet among themselves in all points they do not accord.[2]

---

[1] *deceitful divination.* From Roper (p. 11) and from Stapleton (p. 103) we learn More's interest in astronomy, from his epigrams his contempt for astrologers.

[2] *do not accord.* All this is vague enough. Of the ancient philosophers some, like Democritus and Lucretius, thought that the world was formed by the fortuitous coalescence of atoms which were eternal; others, like Plato, thought that God working through the Demiurge produced it from matter which had existed from eternity; others, like Plotinus and Porphyry, thought the world to be an emanation from God. Aristotle's views are doubtful.

Even among Christian philosophers there have been disputes. Thus Peter Lombard, following the Arabian

In that part of philosophy which entreateth of manners and virtue, their reasons and opinions agree with ours. They dispute of the good qualities of the soul, of the body, and of fortune ; and whether the name of goodness may be applied to all these, or only to the endowments and gifts of the soul. They reason of virtue and pleasure. But the chief and principal question is in what thing, be it one or more, the felicity of man consisteth. But in this point they seem almost too much given and inclined to the opinion of them which defend pleasure,[1] wherein they determine either all or the chiefest part of man's felicity to rest. And (which is more to be marvelled at) the defence of this so dainty and delicate an opinion they fetch even from their grave, sharp, bitter, and

---

Avicenna, held that God could communicate to a creature the power to create. St. Thomas Aquinas expresses his dissent from this view in I^a, Q. xlv, a. 5, but it is not heretical. Again, although all agree that in fact the world was created by God in time, yet some, like Aquinas himself (I^a, Q. xlvi, a. 2), have held that it cannot be proved to be against reason that the world should have been created from eternity ; others, like St. Albert the Great and St. Bonaventure, utterly deny the possibility of creation from eternity.

[1] *which defend pleasure.* The chief and best-known schools of ancient philosophy were the Stoics and their rivals the Epicureans. The Utopians, with the latter, make pleasure their end, and yet, with the former, hold virtue to be the highest good. More tries to reconcile these two views by religion. (See a few lines further on.) Richard Pace wrote of him, ' There is no school of philosophy of which he does not in some part approve.' (*De Fructu Doctrinae*, 1517). It should be noted that More makes Hythloday disapprove of the hedonism of the Utopians. They are *propensiores aequo*, i.e. ' more inclined to it than is right.'

rigorous religion.[1]   For they never dispute of
felicity or blessedness, but they join unto the reasons
of philosophy certain principles taken out of
religion ; without the which to the investigation
of true felicity they think reason of itself weak and
imperfect.

Those principles be these and suchlike. That
the soul is immortal,[2] and by the bountiful goodness
of God ordained to felicity. That to our virtues
and good deeds rewards be appointed after this
life, and to our evil deeds punishments. Though
these be pertaining to religion, yet they think it
meet that they should be believed and granted by
proofs of reason.[3]   But if these principles were

[1] *their grave . . . religion.* The word 'their' distort[s]
More's meaning, which is not that the Utopian religion i[s]
especially sombre, but that religion in general is so. Henc[e]
it is strange to find arguments for hedonism drawn from it·

[2] *soul is immortal.* A marginal note comments, 'a matter
about which nowadays many, even among Christians, doubt
or dispute.' Professor Chambers (p. 135) notes the remark-
able coincidence that almost simultaneously with the *Utopia*
there appeared at Bologna (November 6, 1516) a book by
Pietro Pomponazzi, the well-known professor of philosophy
at that university, on the Immortality of the Soul, in which,
while professing to submit to the Church in matters of
faith, he yet claimed the right, as a philosopher, to doubt
about immortality. Moreover, the subject had come before
the Fifth Lateran Council, which sat from 1512 to 1517.
On December 19, 1513, it condemned the error that the
rational or intellectual soul is mortal. The text can be
read in Denzinger, *Enchiridion Symbolorum.*

[3] *by proofs of reason.* More writes that religion and reason
support each other. Reason cannot decide upon the nature
of true happiness except with the help of religion, and
religion in turn needs the help of reason. Robinson's
translation is not quite accurate. More did not write that

condemned and disannulled, then without any delay they pronounce no man to be so foolish, which would not do all his diligence and endeavour to obtain pleasure by right or wrong, only avoiding this inconvenience, that the less pleasure should not be a let or hindrance to the bigger ; or that he laboured not for that pleasure which would bring after it displeasure, grief, and sorrow. For they judge it extreme madness to follow sharp and painful virtue, and not only to banish the pleasure of life, but also willingly to suffer grief, without any hope of profit thereof ensuing. For what profit can there be, if a man, when he hath passed over all his life unpleasantly, that is to say, miserably, shall have no reward after his death ?

But now, sir, they think not felicity to rest in all pleasure, but only in that pleasure that is good and honest, and that hereto, as to perfect blessedness,

---

men believe on grounds of reason, but that reason leads them on (*perducere*) to belief, that is, by removing difficulties, by marshalling arguments, etc., so that the act of faith may be 'a reasonable service.' (*Rom.* xii, 1.)

The truth here spoken of, the immortality of the soul and its reception of rewards or punishments after death, is a matter of natural religion, which men can get to know by the proper use of their natural faculties, without the supernatural enlightenment of revelation. Revelation, nevertheless, enables man to know this truth, more surely, more easily, and with less admixture of error. The other truth of similar character is that of the existence of God (see below, p. 201). Of these truths we read in the *Epistle to the Hebrews* (xi, 6) : ' Without faith it is impossible to please God ; for he that cometh to God must believe that he is, and is a rewarder to them that seek him.' Our saint wishes to contrast the firm belief of the poor pagan Utopians who had but reason as their guide, with the doubts of so-called Christians.

M

our nature is allured and drawn even of virtue,
whereto only[1] they that be of the contrary opinion
do attribute felicity. For they define virtue to be
life ordered according to nature, and that we be
hereunto ordained of God. And that he doth follow
the course of nature, which in desiring and refusing
things is ruled by reason.

Furthermore that reason doth chiefly and principally kindle in men the love and veneration of the
divine Majesty. Of whose goodness it is that we
be, and that we be in possibility to attain felicity.
And that secondarily it both stirreth and provoketh
us to lead our life out of care in joy and mirth,
and also moveth us to help and further all other in
respect of the society of nature to obtain and enjoy
the same. For there was never man so earnest and
painful a follower of virtue and hater of pleasure,
that would so enjoin your labours, watchings, and
fastings, but he would also exhort you to ease,
lighten, and relieve, to your power, the lack and
misery of others,[2] praising the same as a deed of
humanity and pity. Then if it be a point of humanity
for man to bring health and comfort to man, and
specially (which is a virtue most peculiarly belonging
to man) to mitigate and assuage the grief of others,
and by taking from them the sorrow and heaviness
of life, to restore them to joy, that is to say to

[1] *whereto only*. Robinson probably means that in virtue
alone did they place true happiness. Thus he takes More's
sola as if it were *soli*, as also does Burnet. Delcourt prints
soli (p. 141).

[2] *misery of others*. In the *Dialogue of Comfort* More sets
himself to answer the objection that if tribulation have such
excellent uses we should pray that our neighbour should
have misfortune rather than prosperity (p. 44).

pleasure; why may it not then be said that nature doth provoke every man to do the same to himself? For a joyful life, that is to say, a pleasant life is either evil; and if it be so, then thou shouldest not only help no man thereto, but rather, as much as in thee lieth, withdraw all men from it, as noisome and hurtful; or else if thou not only mayest, but also of duty art bound to procure it to others, why not chiefly to thyself? To whom thou art bound to show as much favour and gentleness as to others. For when nature biddeth thee to be good and gentle to others she commandeth thee not to be cruel and ungentle to thyself.

Therefore even very nature (say they) prescribeth to us a joyful life, that is to say, pleasure as the end of all our operations. And they define virtue to be life ordered according to the prescript of nature. But in that that nature doth allure and provoke men one to help another to live merrily (which surely she doth not without a good cause: for no man is so far above the lot of man's state or condition, that nature doth cark[1] and care for him only, which equally favoureth all that be comprehended under the communion of one shape, form, and fashion), verily she commandeth thee to use diligent circumspection, that thou do not so seek for thine own commodities that thou procure others' incommodities.

Wherefore their opinion is, that not only covenants and bargains made among private men ought to be well and faithfully fulfilled, observed, and kept, but also common laws, which either a

---

[1] *cark.* A synonym for the 'care' which follows. The Latin employs but a single word.

good prince hath justly published, or else the
people neither oppressed with tyranny, neither
deceived by fraud and guile, hath by their common
consent constituted and ratified, concerning the
partition of the commodities of life, that is to say,
the matter[1] of pleasure. These laws not offended,
it is wisdom that thou look to thine own wealth.
And to do the same for the commonwealth is no
less than thy duty, if thou bearest any reverent
love, or any natural zeal and affection to thy
native country. But to go about to let another
man of[2] his pleasure, whilst thou procurest thine
own, that is open wrong.

Contrariwise to withdraw something from thyself
to give to others, that is a point of humanity and
gentleness; which never taketh away so much
commodity as it bringeth again. For it is recompensed with the return of benefits, and the conscience
of the good deed, with the remembrance of the
thankful love and benevolence of them to whom
thou hast done it, doth bring more pleasure to
thy mind, than that which thou hast withholden
from thyself could have brought to thy body.
Finally (which to a godly disposed and a religious
mind is easy to be persuaded), God recompenseth
the gift of a short and small pleasure with great
and everlasting joy. Therefore, the matter diligently
weighed and considered, thus they think that all
our actions, and in them the virtues themselves
be referred at the last to pleasure, as their end and
felicity.

Pleasure they call every motion and state of the

[1] *the matter*. The material.
[2] *to let another man of*. To hinder another man's pleasure.

body or mind, wherein man hath naturally delectation. Appetite they join to nature, and that not
without a good cause. For like as, not only the
senses, but also right reason coveteth whatsoever
is naturally pleasant, so that it may be gotten
without wrong or injury, not letting or debarring
a greater pleasure, nor causing painful labour, even
so those things that men by vain imagination do
feign against nature to be pleasant (as though it
lay in their power to change the things, as they
do the names of things), all such pleasures they
believe to be of so small help and furtherance
to felicity, that they count them a great let and
hindrance, because that, in whom they have once
taken place, all his mind they possess with a false
opinion of pleasure. So that there is no place left
for true and natural delectations. For there be
many things which of their own nature contain no
pleasantness ; yea, the most part of them much
grief and sorrow. And yet through the perverse
and malicious flickering enticements of lewd and
unhonest desires be taken not only for special and
sovereign pleasures, but also be counted among the
chief causes of life.

In this counterfeit kind of pleasure they put
them that I spake of before. Which the better
gowns they have on, the better men they think
themselves. In the which thing they do twice
err. For they be no less deceived in that they
think their gown the better, than they be in that
they think themselves the better. For if you
consider the profitable use of the garment, why
should wool of a finer spun thread be thought
better than the wool of a coarse spun thread ?

Yet they, as though the one did pass the other
by nature, and not by their mistaking, advance
themselves, and think the price of their own persons
thereby greatly increased. And therefore the
honour, which in a coarse gown they durst not
have looked for, they require, as it were of duty,
for their finer gown's sake. And if they be passed
by without reverence, they take it displeasantly
and disdainfully.

And again is it not like madness to take a pride
in vain and unprofitable honours ? For what
natural or true pleasure dost thou take of another
man's bare head[1] or bowed knees ? Will this ease
the pain of thy knees, or remedy the frenzy of
thy head ? In this image of counterfeit pleasure,
they be of a marvellous madness, which for the
opinion of nobility, rejoice much in their own
conceit. Because it was their fortune to come of
such ancestors, whose stock of long time hath
been counted rich (for now nobility is nothing
else), specially rich in lands. And though their
ancestors left them not one foot of land, or else
they themselves have pissed it against the walls,[2]
yet they think themselves not the less noble therefore
of one hair.

In this number also they count them that take

---

[1] *bare head.* Elsewhere (*Dialogue of Comfort*, p. 209)
More writes, probably autobiographically, ' I wist once a
great officer of the King's say . . . that twenty men standing
barehead before him, keep not his head half so warm as
to keep on his own cap. Nor he never took so much ease
with their being barehead before him, as he caught once
grief with a cough that came upon him by standing barehead
long before the King.'

[2] *against the walls.* That is, ' squandered it.'

pleasure and delight (as I said) in gems and precious
stones, and think themselves almost gods, if they
chance to get an excellent one, specially of that
kind which in that time of their own countrymen
is had in highest estimation. For one kind of
stone keepeth not his price still in all countries
and at all times. Nor they buy them not, but
taken out of the gold and bare : no nor so neither,
until they have made the seller to swear that he
will warrant and assure it to be a true stone, and
no counterfeit gem. Such care they take lest a
counterfeit stone should deceive their eyes instead
of a right stone. But why shouldest thou not take
even as much pleasure in beholding a counterfeit
stone which thine eye cannot discern from a right
stone ? They should both be of like value to thee,
even as to the blind man.

What shall I say of them that keep superfluous
riches, to take delectation only in the beholding,
and not in the use or occupying thereof ? Do
they take true pleasure, or else be they deceived
with false pleasure ? Or of them that be in a
contrary vice, hiding the gold which they shall
never occupy, nor peradventure never see more ?
And whilst they take care lest they shall lose it, do
lose it indeed. For what is it else, when they hide
it in the ground, taking it both from their own use,
and perchance from all other men's also ? And yet
thou, when thou hast hid thy treasure, as one
out of all care, hoppest for joy. The which treasure,
if it should chance to be stolen, and thou, ignorant
of the theft, shouldest die ten years after : all that
ten years' space that thou livedst after thy money
was stolen, what matter was it to thee whether

it had been taken away or else safe as thou leftest
it ? Truly both ways like profit came to thee.

To these so foolish pleasures they join dicers,
whose madness they know by hearsay, and not by
use. Hunters also, and hawkers. For what pleasure
is there (say they) in casting the dice upon a table.
Which thou hast done so often, that if there were
any pleasure in it, yet the oft use might make thee
weary thereof ? Or what delight can there be, and
not rather displeasure in hearing the barking and
howling of dogs ? Or what greater pleasure is
there to be felt, when a dog followeth a hare, than
when a dog followeth a dog ? For one thing is
done in both, that is to say, running, if thou hast
pleasure therein. But if the hope of slaughter
and the expectation of tearing in pieces the beast
doth please thee, thou shouldest rather be moved
with pity to see a silly,[1] innocent hare murdered
of a dog, the weak of the stronger, the fearful of
the fierce, the innocent of the cruel and unmerciful.
Therefore all this exercise of hunting, as a thing
unworthy to be used of free men, the Utopians
have rejected to their butchers, to the which craft
(as we said before) they appoint their bondsmen.
For they count hunting the lowest, the vilest, and
most abject part of butchery, and the other parts
of it more profitable, and more honest, as bringing
much more commodity, in that they kill beasts
only for necessity. Whereas the hunter seeketh

[1] *silly*. Poor, pitiable. More himself loved animals, and
had in his garden a collection of various creatures which
afforded him much delight. The Nostell Priory family
group (after the famous Holbein sketch) shows spaniels
at his feet.

nothing but pleasure of the silly and woeful beasts'
slaughter and murder. The which pleasure in
beholding death they think doth rise in the very
beasts, either of a cruel affection of mind, or else
to be changed in continuance of time into cruelty,
by long use of so cruel a pleasure.

These therefore and all such like, which be
innumerable, though the common sort of people
doth take them for pleasures, yet they, seeing there
is no natural pleasantness in them, do plainly
determine them to have no affinity with true and
right pleasure. For as touching that they do
commonly move the sense with delectation (which
seemeth to be a work of pleasure) this doth nothing
diminish their opinion. For not the nature of the
thing, but their perverse and lewd custom is the
cause hereof. Which causeth them to accept bitter
or sour things for sweet things. Even as women
with child in their vitiate and corrupt taste, think
pitch and tallow sweeter than any honey. Howbeit
no man's judgment depraved and corrupt, either by
sickness or by custom, can change the nature of
pleasure, more than it can do the nature of other
things.

They make divers kinds of pleasures. For some
they attribute to the soul, and some to the body.
To the soul they give intelligence, and that delectation that cometh of the contemplation of truth.
Hereunto is joined the pleasant remembrance of
the good life past.[1]

The pleasure of the body they divide into two
parts. The first is when delectation is sensibly

---

[1] *good life past.* Robinson omits the phrase that follows,
' and the sure hope of future happiness.'

felt and perceived. Which many times chanceth
by the renewing and refreshing of those parts
which our natural heat drieth up. This cometh by
meat and drink. And sometimes while those things
be expulsed, and voided, whereof is in the body
over great abundance. This pleasure is felt when
we do our natural easement, or when we be doing
the act of generation, or when the itching of any
part is eased with rubbing or scratching. Sometimes
pleasure riseth, exhibiting to any member nothing
that it desireth, nor taking from it any pain that
it feeleth, which nevertheless tickleth and moveth
our senses with a certain secret efficacy, but with a
manifest motion turneth them to it, as is that
which cometh of music.

The second part of bodily pleasure, they say,
is that which consisteth and resteth in the quiet
and upright state of the body. And that truly is
every man's own proper health intermingled and
disturbed with no grief. For this, if it be not letted
nor assaulted with no grief, is delectable of itself,
though it be moved with no external or outward
pleasure. For though it be not so plain and manifest
to the sense as the greedy lust of eating and drinking,
yet nevertheless many take it for the chiefest
pleasure. All the Utopians grant it to be a right
sovereign pleasure, and as you would say the
foundation and ground of all pleasures, as which
even alone is able to make the state and condition
of life delectable and pleasant. And it being once
taken away, there is no place left for any pleasure.
For to be without grief not having health, that
they call unsensibility, and not pleasure.

The Utopians have long ago rejected and con-

demned the opinion of them which said that
steadfast and quiet health (for this question also
hath been diligently debated among them) ought
not therefore to be counted a pleasure, because
they say it cannot be presently and sensibly perceived
and felt by some outward motion.[1]   But of the
contrary part now they agree almost all in this,
that health is a most sovereign pleasure.   For seeing
that in sickness (say they) is grief, which is a
mortal enemy to pleasure, even as sickness is to
health, why should not then pleasure be in the
quietness of health ?   For they say it maketh nothing
to this matter, whether you say that sickness is a
grief, or that in sickness is grief, for all cometh to
one purpose.   For whether health be a pleasure
itself, or a necessary cause of pleasure, as fire is of
heat, truly both ways it followeth, that they cannot
be without pleasure that be in perfect health.
Furthermore, whilst we eat (say they) then health,
which began to be appaired, fighteth by the help
of food against hunger.   In the which fight, whilst
health by little and little getteth the upper hand,
that same proceeding, and (as you would say) that
onwardness to the wonted strength ministereth
that pleasure whereby we be so refreshed.   Health,
therefore, which in the conflict is joyful, shall it
not be merry when it hath got the victory ?   But
as soon as it hath recovered the pristinate strength,
which thing only in all the fight it coveted, shall it
incontinent be astonied ?   Nor shall it not know
nor embrace the own wealth and goodness ?

---

[1] *by some outward motion.*   Should be ' except by some
outward motion,' or, better still, according to the reading of
Dr. Lupton's Latin edition, ' except by some opposite motion.'

For where it is said, health cannot be felt; this, they think, is nothing true. For what man waking, say they, feeleth not himself in health, but he that is not? Is there any man so possessed with stonish insensibility, or with lethargy, that is to say, the sleeping sickness, that he will not grant health to be acceptable to him and delectable? But what other thing is delectation than that which by another name is called pleasure?

They embrace chiefly the pleasures of the mind. For them they count the chiefest and most principal of all. The chief part of them they think doth come of the exercise of virtue, and conscience of good life. Of these pleasures that the body ministereth, they give the pre-eminence to health. For the delight of eating and drinking, and whatsoever hath any like pleasantness, they determine to be pleasures much to be desired, but no other ways than for health's sake. For such things of their own proper nature be not so pleasant, but in that they resist sickness privily stealing on. Therefore like as it is a wise man's part, rather to avoid sickness than to wish for medicines, and rather to drive away and put to flight careful griefs than to call for comfort; so it is much better not to need this kind of pleasure than thereby to be eased of the contrary grief. The which kind of pleasure, if any man take for his felicity, that man must needs grant, that then he shall be in most felicity, if he live that life which is led in continual hunger, thirst, itching, eating, drinking, scratching, and rubbing. The which life how not only foul and unhonest, but also how miserable and wretched it is, who perceiveth not? These doubtless be the basest pleasures of all, as unpure and unperfect. For they never come, but accompanied with their contrary griefs. As with the pleasure of eating is joined hunger, and that after no very equal sort. For of these two the grief is both the more vehement, and also of longer continuance. For it beginneth before the pleasure, and endeth not until the pleasure die with it.

Wherefore such pleasures they think not greatly to be set by, but in that they be necessary. Howbeit they have delight also in these, and thankfully knowledge the tender love of mother nature, which with most pleasant delectation allureth her children to that, to the necessary use whereof they must from time to time continually be forced and driven. For how wretched and miserable should our life be, if these daily griefs of hunger and thirst could not be driven away, but with bitter potions and sour medicines, as the other diseases be, wherewith we be seldomer troubled?

But beauty, strength, nimbleness, these as peculiar and pleasant gifts of nature they make much of. But those pleasures that be received by the ears, the eyes, and the nose, which nature willeth to be proper and peculiar to man (for no other living creature doth behold the fairness and the beauty of the world, or is moved with any respect of savours, but only for the diversity of meats, neither perceiveth the concordant and discordant distances of sounds and tunes), these pleasures, I say, they accept and allow as certain pleasant rejoicings[1] of life.

---

[1] *rejoicings.* The Latin word *condimenta* recalls More's advice to his children that they should take virtue and learning for their meat, play but for their sauce.

But in all things this cautel they use, that a less pleasure hinder not a bigger, and that the pleasure be no cause of displeasure, which they think to follow of necessity, if the pleasure be unhonest. But yet to despise the comeliness of beauty, to waste the bodily strength, to turn nimbleness into sluggishness, to consume and make feeble the body with fasting, to do injury to health, and to reject the pleasant motions of nature ; unless a man neglect these commodities, whiles he doth with a fervent zeal procure the wealth of others, or the common profit, for the which pleasure forborne, he is in hope of a greater pleasure at God's hand ; else for a vain shadow of virtue, for the wealth and profit of no man, to punish himself, or to the intent he may be able courageously to suffer adversity, which perchance shall never come to him, this to do they think it a point of extreme madness, and a token of a man cruelly minded towards himself, and unkind towards nature, as one so disdaining to be in her danger that he renounceth and refuseth all her benefits.

This is their sentence and opinion of virtue and pleasure. And they believe that by man's reason none can be found truer than this, unless any godlier be inspired[1] into man from heaven. Wherein

[1] *unless any godlier be inspired*. This sentence, marked in the Louvain edition of the Latin works (1566) with the marginal note *Adnotandum et hoc diligenter*, ' This is to be particularly noted,' shows once again how carefully More distinguishes Utopian customs, inspired by unaided reason, from any that might be adopted as a consequence of divine revelation.

According to Catholic doctrine, asceticism is not an end in itself, but a means to an end, whether that end be self-

whether they believe well or no, neither the time doth suffer us to discuss, neither it is now necessary. For we have taken upon us to show and declare their laws and ordinances, and not to defend them.

But this thing I believe verily : howsoever these decrees be, that there is in no place of the world, neither a more excellent people, neither a more flourishing commonwealth. They be light and quick of body, full of activity and nimbleness, and of more strength than a man would judge them by their stature, which, for all that, is not too low. And though their soil be not very fruitful, nor their air very wholesome, yet against the air they so defend them with temperate diet, and so order and husband their ground with diligent travail, that in no country is greater increase and plenty of corn and cattle, nor men's bodies of longer life, and subject or apt to fewer diseases.

There, therefore, a man may see well and dili-gently exploited and furnished, not only those things which husbandmen do commonly in other

control, expiation for personal sin or the sins of others. We have a duty to take reasonable care of life and health, as may be illustrated by St. John Fisher's taking extra food and wearing extra clothing as he was about to set out for his martyrdom on Tower Hill ! By asceticism to do serious injury to the health is condemned by Catholic teaching just as much as by the Utopians. Some of the saints have after-wards confessed that their mortifications were excessive. Yet the harm done by excessive penance must weigh very lightly in comparison with the harm wrought by over-indulgence. (See C.T.S. pamphlet *Penance and Fasting*, by P. E. Hallett.) More consistently practised severe penance, both in his youth, when he was as yet, according to a certain class of writers, untrammelled by superstition, and to the very end of his life. (Stapleton, pp. 9 and 206.)

countries, as by craft and cunning to remedy the barrenness of the ground; but also a whole wood by the hands of the people plucked up by the roots in one place, and set again in another place. Wherein was had regard and consideration, not of plenty, but of commodious carriage, that wood and timber might be nigher to the sea, or the rivers, or the cities. For it is less labour and business to carry grain far by land, than wood. The people be gentle, merry, quick, and fine-witted, delighting in quietness, and when need requireth, able to abide and suffer much bodily labour. Else they be not greatly desirous and fond of it; but in the exercise and study of the mind they be never weary.

When they had heard me speak of the Greek literature or learning (for in Latin, there was nothing that I thought they would greatly allow, besides historians and poets) they made wonderful, earnest, and importunate suit unto me that I would teach and instruct them in that tongue and learning. I began, therefore, to read unto them, at the first truly more because I would not seem to refuse the labour, than that I hoped that they would anything profit therein. But when I had gone forward a little, I perceived incontinent by their diligence, that my labour should not be bestowed in vain. For they began so easily to fashion their letters, so plainly to pronounce the words, so quickly to learn by heart, and so surely to rehearse the same, that I marvelled at it, saving that the most part of them were fine and chosen wits, and of ripe age, picked out of the company of the learned men, which not only of their own free and voluntary will, but also by the commandment of the council, undertook to learn this language. Therefore in less than three years' space there was nothing in the Greek tongue that they lacked. They were able to read good authors without any stay, if the book were not false.

This kind of learning, as I suppose, they took so much the sooner, because it is somewhat alliant to them. For I think that this nation took their beginning of the Greeks, because their speech, which in all other points is not much unlike the Persian tongue, keepeth divers signs and tokens of the Greek language in the names of their cities and of their magistrates.

They have of me (for when I was determined to enter into my fourth voyage, I cast into the ship in the stead of merchandise a pretty fardel of books, because I intended to come again rather never than shortly), they have, I say, of me the most part of Plato's works, more of Aristotle's, also Theophrastus of plants, but in divers places (which I am sorry for) imperfect. For whilst we were aship board, a marmoset chanced upon the book, as it was negligently laid by, which, wantonly playing therewith, plucked out certain leaves, and tore them in pieces. Of them that have written the grammar, they have only Lascaris. For Theodorus I carried not with me, nor never a dictionary, but Hesychius, and Dioscorides. They set great store by Plutarch's books. And they be delighted with Lucian's merry conceits[1] and jests. Of the poets they have Aristophanes, Homer, Euripides, and Sophocles in

---

[1] *delighted with Lucian's merry conceits.* As was More himself, for he translated some of his works and wrote imitations. Lucian refused to take Plato seriously.

N

Aldus's[1] small print. Of the historians they have
Thucydides, Herodotus, and Herodian. Also my
companion, Tricius Apinatus,[2] carried with him
physic books, certain small works of Hippocrates,
and Galenus's Microtechne. The which book they
have in great estimation.

For though there be almost no nation under
heaven that hath less need of physic than they,
yet this notwithstanding, physic is nowhere in
greater honour. Because they count the knowledge
of it among the goodliest and most profitable parts
of philosophy. For whilst they by the help of this
philosophy search out the secret mysteries of
nature, they think themselves to receive thereby
not only wonderful great pleasure, but also to
obtain great thanks and favour of the author and
maker thereof. Whom they think, according to the
fashion of other artificers, to have set forth the
marvellous and gorgeous frame of the world[3] for
man with great affection intentively to behold,
whom only he hath made of wit and capacity to
consider and understand the excellency of so great
a work. And therefore he beareth (say they) more
goodwill and love to the curious and diligent

---

[1] *Aldus.* A famous early Venetian printer.

[2] *Tricius Apinatus.* More coined the name. Trica and
Apina were two towns of Apulia so insignificant that they
passed into a proverb for worthlessness. (Dr. Lupton.)

[3] *gorgeous frame of the world.* Compare *Wisdom* xiii, 1
(referred to by St. Paul in *Romans* i, 18): 'But all men are
vain in whom there is not the knowledge of God : and who,
by these good things that are seen, could not understand
him that is, etc.' Or the whole of Psalm viii, beginning,
' O Lord our God, how admirable is Thy name in the whole
earth.'

beholder and viewer of his work, and marveller at the same, than he doth to him, which like a very brute beast, without wit and reason, or as one without sense or moving, hath no regard to so great and so wonderful a spectacle.

The wits, therefore, of the Utopians, inured and exercised in learning, be marvellous quick in the invention of feats helping anything to the advantage and wealth of life. Howbeit two feats they may thank us for. That is the science of imprinting, and the craft of making paper. And yet not only us, but chiefly and principally themselves.

For when we showed to them Aldus's print in books of paper, and told them of the stuff whereof paper is made, and of the feat of graving letters, speaking somewhat more than we could plainly declare (for there was none of us that knew perfectly either the one or the other), they forthwith very wittily conjectured the thing. And whereas before they wrote only in skins, in barks of trees, and in reeds, now they have attempted to make paper, and to imprint letters. And though at the first it proved not all of the best, yet, by often assaying the same, they shortly got the feat of both. And have so brought the matter about, that if they had copies of Greek authors, they could lack no books. But now they have no more than I rehearsed before, saving that by printing of books they have multiplied and increased the same into many thousands of copies.

Whosoever cometh thither to see the land, being excellent in any gift of wit, or through much and long journeying well experienced and seen in the knowledge of many countries (for the which cause we were very welcome to them), him they receive and entertain wondrous gently and lovingly. For they have delight to hear what is done in every land, howbeit very few merchantmen come thither. For what should they bring thither, unless it were iron, or else gold and silver, which they had rather carry home again? Also such things as are to be carried out of their land, they think it more wisdom to carry that gear forth themselves, than that others should come thither to fetch it, to the intent they may the better know the outlands on every side of them, and keep in ure[1] the feat and knowledge of sailing.

[1] *ure*. Practice, employment. The words 'inured,' 'manœuvre' are from the same root. It is not the same word as 'use.'

OF BONDMEN, SICK PERSONS, WEDLOCK, AND DIVERS OTHER MATTERS

THEY neither make bondmen of prisoners taken in battle, unless it be in battle that they fought themselves, nor of bondmen's children, nor, to be short, of any such as they can get out of foreign countries, though he were there a bondman. But either such as among themselves for heinous offences be punished with bondage, or else such as in the cities of other lands for great trespasses be condemned to death. And of this sort of bondmen they have most store. For many of them they bring home, sometimes paying very little for them, yea, most commonly getting them for gramercy. These sorts of bondmen they keep not only in continual work and labour, but also in bands. But their own men they handle hardest, whom they judge more desperate, and to have deserved greater punishment, because they being so godly brought up to virtue in so excellent a commonwealth, could not for all that be refrained from misdoing.

Another kind of bondman they have, when a vile drudge being a poor labourer in another country doth choose of his own free will to be a bondman among them. These they entreat and order honestly, and entertain almost as gently as their own free citizens, saving that they put them to a

little more labour, as thereto accustomed. If any
such be disposed to depart thence (which seldom
is seen), they neither hold him against his will,
neither send him away with empty hands.

The sick (as I said) they see to with great affection,
and let nothing at all pass concerning either physic
or good diet, whereby they may be restored again
to their health. Such as be sick of incurable diseases
they comfort with sitting by them, with talking
with them, and, to be short, with all manner of
helps that may be. But if the disease be not only
incurable, but also full of continual pain and
anguish, then the priests and the magistrates exhort
the man, seeing he is not able to do any duty of
life, and by overliving his own death is noisome
and irksome to others, and grievous to himself,
that he will determine with himself no longer to
cherish that pestilent and painful disease. And
seeing his life is to him but a torment, that he will
not be unwilling to die, but rather take a good hope
to him, and either despatch himself out of that
painful life,[1] as out of a prison, or a rack of torment

---

[1] *despatch himself out of that painful life.* More's treatment
of this matter of suicide is an excellent instance of the danger
to which so many writers have succumbed, of imagining
that customs Hythloday ascribed to the Utopians met with
More's considered approval. Bearing in mind the essential
distinction between what reason can attain and what revelation adds to this, the most that we can say here is that perhaps
More did not see how suicide, under the carefully guarded
conditions under which it was practised in Utopia, could
be condemned on the grounds of reason alone. Notoriously
it was approved by the Stoics. Even Plato, though condemning it in general, clearly thinks it justifiable in special cases.
(*Laws*, Book IX, p. 384.)

But More is quite clear about God's law. Even in the

or else suffer himself willingly to be rid out of it by
others. And in so doing they tell him he shall do
wisely, seeing by his death he shall lose no commodity, but end his pain. And because in that act
he shall follow the counsel of the priests, that is to
say, of the interpreters of God's will and pleasure,
they show him that he shall do like a godly and a
virtuous man.

They that be thus persuaded, finish their lives
willingly, either with hunger, or else die in their
sleep without any feeling of death. But they cause
none such to die against his will, nor they use no
less diligence and attendance about him, believing
this to be an honourable death. Else he that killeth
himself before that the priests and the counsel have
allowed the cause of his death, him as unworthy
either to be buried, or with fire to be consumed, they
cast unburied into some stinking marsh.

The woman is not married before she be eighteen
years old. The man is four years older before he
marry. If either the man or the woman be proved
to have actually offended before their marriage,

Utopia itself he enunciates it : ' Whereas, by the permission
of God, no man neither hath power to kill neither himself,
nor yet any other man, etc.' (See above, p. 56.) St.
Augustine treated the subject fully in *De Civitate Dei*, Book I,
Chapters XVI to XXVI, dealing with certain objections
drawn from Holy Scripture and from the deaths of some
of the martyrs. So strict a view does he adopt that he is
ready to condemn the act of the Christian virgins who (it
is said) threw themselves into the fire rather than suffer
the violation of their chastity, unless they acted under divine
inspiration. More, too, deals with the matter in his *Dialogue
of Comfort*, and it is important to note that he quotes St.
Augustine's solution of the objections we have just mentioned
and agrees with them (p. 135).

with another,[1] the party that so hath trespassed is
sharply punished. And both the offenders be
forbidden ever after in all their life to marry,
unless the fault be forgiven by the prince's pardon.
But both the goodman and the goodwife of the
house where that offence was committed, as being
slack and negligent in looking to their charge,
be in danger of great reproach and infamy. That
offence is so sharply punished, because they perceive,
that unless they be diligently kept from the liberty
of this vice, few will join together in the love of
marriage, wherein all the life must be led with one,
and also all the griefs and displeasures coming
therewith patiently be taken and borne.

Furthermore in choosing wives and husbands
they observe earnestly and straightly a custom
which seemed to us very fond and foolish.[2] For
a sad and honest matron showeth the woman, be
she maid or widow, naked to the wooer. And
likewise a sage and discreet man exhibiteth the
wooer naked to the woman. At this custom we
laughed, and disallowed it as foolish.

But they on the other part do greatly wonder at
the folly of all other nations, which in buying a colt,

---

[1] *with another*. These words are added by the translator
without any warrant. The Utopian law is very strict.
Unchastity, even between engaged couples, involves the
life-long penalty of enforced celibacy.

[2] *fond and foolish*. The Latin adjectives are even stronger,
ineptissimum adprimeque ridiculum, 'most inept and utterly
ridiculous.' More is clearly joking, though it may be that
he wished to insist on the self-mastery of the poor pagan
Utopians who could practise without danger (see the strict
law spoken of in previous note), a custom that even to
Christians would be an intolerable strain.

whereas a little money is in hazard, be so chary and circumspect, that though he be almost all bare, yet they will not buy him, unless the saddle and all the harness be taken off, lest under those coverings be hid some gall or sore. And yet in choosing a wife, which shall be either pleasure or displeasure to them all their life after, they be so reckless, that all the residue of the woman's body being covered with clothes, they esteem her scarcely by one handbreadth (for they can see no more but her face), and so to join her to them not without great jeopardy of evil agreeing together, if anything in her body afterward should chance to offend and mislike them. For all men be not so wise as to have respect to the virtuous conditions of the party. And the endowments of the body cause the virtues of the mind more to be esteemed and regarded, yea, even in the marriages of wise men. Verily so foul deformity may be hid under those coverings, that it may quite alienate and take away the man's mind from his wife, when it shall not be lawful for their bodies to be separate again. If such deformity happen by any chance after the marriage is consummate and finished, well, there is no remedy but patience. Every man must take his fortune well a worth. But it were well done that a law were made whereby all such deceits might be eschewed and avoided beforehand.

And this were they constrained more earnestly to look upon, because they only of the nations in that part of the world be content every man with one wife apiece. And matrimony is there never broken, but by death ; except adultery break the bond, or else the intolerable wayward manners of either party. For if either of them find themselves for any such cause grieved, they may by the licence of the council change and take another. But the other party liveth ever after in infamy and out of wedlock. Howbeit the husband to put away his wife for no other fault, but for that some mishap is fallen to her body, this by no means they will suffer. For they judge it a great point of cruelty, that anybody in their most need of help and comfort should be cast off and forsaken, and that old age, which both bringeth sickness with it, and is a sickness itself, should unkindly and unfaithfully be dealt withal.

But now and then it chanceth, whereas the man and the woman cannot well agree between themselves, both of them finding other with whom they hope to live more quietly and merrily, that they by the full consent of them both be divorced asunder and married again to other.[1] But that not without

---

[1] *be divorced asunder and married again to other.* Here again, as with the matter of suicide, if More is to be considered as giving his own views through the mouth of Hythloday, it can only mean that he found it hard to prove, on grounds of natural reason alone, these practices unlawful.

Though it is not the technical charge mentioned in his indictment, yet More was undoubtedly right in stating that his refusal to recognise the King's right to divorce his wife was the ultimate ground of his condemnation to death (Stapleton, p. 197). He was thus a martyr to the sanctity of marriage. Plato recommended divorce and remarriage if husband and wife remained childless for ten years (*Laws*, Book VI, p. 299), but when Luther and Tyndale, in a somewhat similar strain, urged that a husband, who was 'not able to do his duty to his wife' was 'bounden secretly without slander to provide another to do it for him,' More reproached them for this 'and much other beastliness . . . of such sort as honest ears could scant abide the hearing.' (*Dialogue*, E. W., p. 250.)

the authority of the council.   Which agreeth to no
divorces before they and their wives have diligently
tried and examined the matter.   Yea, and then also
they be loth to consent to it, because they know this
to be the next way to break love between man and
wife, to be in easy hope of a new marriage.

Breakers of wedlock be punished with most
grievous bondage.   And if both the offenders were
married, then the parties which in that behalf
have suffered wrong, being divorced from the
advoutrers, be married together, if they will, or else
to whom they lust.   But if either of them both do
still continue in love toward so unkind a bed-
fellow, the use of wedlock is not to them forbidden,
if the party faultless be disposed to follow in toiling
and drudgery the person which for that offence is
condemned to bondage.   And very oft[1] it chanceth
that the repentance of the one, and the earnest
diligence of the other, doth so move the prince with
pity and compassion, that he restoreth the bond
person from servitude to liberty and freedom again.
But if the same party be taken eftsoons in that fault,
there is no other way but death.

To other trespasses no prescript punishment is
appointed by any law.   But according to the
heinousness of the offence, or contrary, so the
punishment is moderated by the discretion of the
council.   The husbands chastise their wives, and
the parents their children, unless they have done
any so horrible an offence that the open punishment
thereof maketh much for the advancement of honest
manners.   But most commonly the most heinous
faults be punished with the incommodity of

[1] *very oft*.   Should be 'From time to time.'

bondage. For that they suppose to be to the offenders
no less grief, and to the commonwealth more profit,
than if they should hastily put them to death, and
so make them quite out of the way. For there
cometh more profit of their labour than of their
death, and by their example they fear other the
longer from like offences. But if they being thus
used, do rebel and kick again, then forsooth they
be slain as desperate and wild beasts, whom neither
prison nor chain could restrain and keep under.
But they which take their bondage patiently be not
left all hopeless. For after they have been broken
and tamed with long miseries, if then they show
such repentance, as thereby it may be perceived
that they be sorrier for their offence than for their
punishment, sometimes by the prince's prerogative,
and sometimes by the voice and consent of the
people, their bondage either is mitigated, or else
clean released and forgiven. He that moveth to[1]
advoutry is in no less danger and jeopardy than if
he had committed advoutry in deed.[2] For in all
offences they count the intent and pretensed purpose
as evil as the act or deed itself, thinking that no let
ought to excuse him that did his best to have no let.

They have singular delight and pleasure in fools.[3]
And as it is a great reproach to do any of them
hurt or injury, so they prohibit not to take pleasure

[1] *moveth to.* As the next sentence shows, the meaning is
' to attempt.'

[2] *if he had committed advoutry in deed.* Compare *Matt.* v, 28 :
' Who so ever looketh on a woman to lust after her, hath
already committed adultery with her in his heart.'

[3] *They have . . . pleasure in fools.* As did More himself,
whose fool Henry Pattenson is in the family group by
Holbein. See Stapleton, p. 97.

of foolishness. For that, they think, doth much good to the fools. And if any man be so sad and stern, that he cannot laugh neither at their words, nor at their deeds, none of them be committed to his tuition, for fear lest he would not entreat them gently and favourably enough ; to whom they should bring no delectation (for other goodness in them is none), much less any profit should they yield him.

To mock a man for his deformity, or for that he lacketh any part or limb of his body, is counted great dishonesty and reproach, not to him that is mocked, but to him that mocketh. Which unwisely doth upbraid any man of that as a vice, that was not in his power to eschew. Also as they count and reckon very little wit to be in him that regardeth not natural beauty and comeliness, so to help the same with paintings is taken for a vain and a wanton pride, not without great infamy. For they know even by very experience that no comeliness of beauty doth so highly commend and advance the wives in the conceit of their husbands, as honest conditions and lowliness. For as love is oftentimes won with beauty, so it is not kept, preserved, and continued but by virtue and obedience.

They do not only fear their people from doing evil by punishments, but also allure them to virtue with rewards of honour. Therefore they set up in the market-place the images of notable men, and of such as have been great and bountiful benefactors to the commonwealth, for the perpetual memory of their good acts : and also that the glory and renown of the ancestors may stir and provoke their posterity

to virtue. He that inordinately and ambitiously
desireth promotions is left all hopeless for ever
attaining any promotion as long as he liveth.

They live together lovingly. For no magistrate
is either haughty or fearful. Fathers they be called,
and like fathers they use themselves. The citizens
(as it is their duty) willingly exhibit unto them due
honour without any compulsion. Nor the prince
himself is not known from the other by princely
apparel, or a robe of state, nor by a crown or
diadem royal, or cap of maintenance, but by a little
sheaf of corn carried before him. And so a taper
of wax is borne before the bishop, whereby only
he is known.

They have but few laws. For to people so
instructed and instituted very few do suffice. Yea,
this thing they chiefly reprove among other nations,
that innumerable books of laws, and expositions
upon the same be not sufficient. But they think it
against all right and justice that men should be
bound to those laws, which either be in number
more than be able to be read, or else blinder and
darker than that any man can well understand them.

Furthermore they utterly exclude and banish all
attorneys,[1] proctors, and sergeants at the law,
which craftily handle matters, and subtly dispute of
the laws. For they think it most meet that every
man should plead his own matter, and tell the same
tale before the judge that he would tell to his man
of law. So shall there be less circumstance of words,

---

[1] *all attorneys, etc.* Robinson uses three words to express
the one Latin word *causidicos*, i.e. pleaders, barristers. That
More, himself a lawyer, tried to avoid the unfairnesses
exposed by Hythloday is apparent from Stapleton (p. 17).

and the truth shall sooner come to light, whilst the
judge with a discreet judgment doth weigh the
words of him whom no lawyer hath instructed with
deceit, and whilst he helpeth and beareth out simple
wits against the false and malicious circumventions
of crafty children.[1]   This is hard to be observed in
other countries, in so infinite a number of blind and
intricate laws.

But in Utopia every man is a cunning lawyer.
For (as I said) they have very few laws; and the
plainer and grosser that any interpretation is, that
they allow as most just. For all laws (say they) be
made and published only to the intent, that by them
every man should be put in remembrance of his
duty. But the crafty and subtle interpretation of
them (forasmuch as few can attain thereto) can put
very few in that remembrance, whereas the simple,
the plain, and gross meaning of the laws is open
to every man. Else as touching the vulgar sort of
the people, which be both most in number, and
have most need to know their duties, were it not as
good for them that no law were made at all, as when
it is made, to bring so blind an interpretation upon

---

[1] *children.* People. In his *Debellacion of Salem and Byzance,*
More gives at some length his reasons for thinking that
commonly justice would be just as surely and more
expeditiously administered if judges could dispense with
juries. ' I never saw the day yet indeed, nor never I trust in
God I shall, but that I may well, and so will I do indeed, trust
the truth of one judge as well as the truth of two juries.'
(E. W., 989.) Father Bridgett's comment is : ' More was to
experience that neither judges nor juries could be trusted
against the king.' (*Wit and Wisdom of Sir T. More*, p. 179n.)
See too More's merry story in the letter to Lady Alington
(E. W., p. 1437).

it, that without great wit and long arguing no man
can discuss it ? To the finding out whereof neither
the gross judgment of the people can attain, neither
the whole life of them that be occupied in working
for their livings can suffice thereto.

These virtues of the Utopians have caused their
next neighbours and borderers, which live free
and under no subjection (for the Utopians long ago
have delivered many of them from tyranny), to
take magistrates of them, some for a year, and
some for five years' space. Which, when the time
of their office is expired, they bring home again
with honour and praise, and take new again with
them into their country.

These nations have undoubtedly very well and
wholesomely provided for their commonwealths.
For seeing that both the making and marring of
the weal public doth depend and hang upon the
manners of the rulers and magistrates, what officers
could they more wisely have chosen than those
which cannot be led from honesty by bribes (for to
them that shortly after shall depart thence into their
own country money should be unprofitable), nor
yet be moved either with favour or malice towards
any man, as being strangers, and unacquainted
with the people ? The which two vices of affection
and avarice, where they take place in judgments,
incontinent they break justice, the strongest and
surest bond of a commonwealth. These people
who fetch their officers and rulers from them, the
Utopians call their fellows. And others to whom
they have been beneficial, they call their friends.

As touching leagues, which in other places
between country and country be so oft concluded,

broken, and renewed, they never make none with
any nation. For to what purpose serve leagues?
say they. As though nature had not set sufficient
love between man and man. And whoso regardeth
not nature, think you that he will pass for words?
They be brought into this opinion chiefly because
that, in those parts of the world, leagues between
princes be wont to be kept and observed very
slenderly.

For here in Europe, and especially in these parts
where the faith and religion of Christ reigneth, the
majesty of leagues is everywhere esteemed holy and
inviolable, partly through the justice and goodness
of princes, and partly at the reverence and motion[1]
of the head bishops. Which like as they make no
promise themselves, but they do very religiously
perform the same, so they exhort all princes in
any wise to abide by their promises, and them that

---

[1] *reverence and motion.* 'Motion' should be 'fear' and
'head bishops' should be translated 'Popes' (*summi
pontifices*). More's sarcasm was fully justified by contemporary political diplomacy, which was, however, so
tangled and complicated that it is not easy now, nor can it
have been even at the time, fairly to assign the blame.
Popes, as More reminded Henry VIII on a famous occasion,
were temporal princes, and had to make leagues with other
States for the defence of their rights. In 1509, Pope Julius II
joined the League of Cambrai against the Venetians. They
were crushed and made their peace with him. In the next
year he turned against France which desired both utterly
to ruin the Venetian republic and to be preponderant in
Italy. A careful reading of the course of events either in
Pastor's *History of the Popes* (Eng. Trans., Vol. VI, pp. 299
et seqq.) or in Brewer's *Reign of Henry VIII* (Vol. I, pp. 12
et seqq.) does not justify the term 'treachery' which some
writers have applied to Julius's conduct.

refuse or deny so to do, by their pontifical power and authority they compel thereto. And surely they think well that it might seem a very reproachful thing, if in the leagues of them which by a peculiar name be called faithful, faith should have no place.

But in that new-found part of the world which is scarcely so far from us beyond the line equinoctial as our life and manners be dissident from theirs, no trust nor confidence is in leagues. But the more and holier ceremonies the league is knit up with, the sooner it is broken by some cavillation found in the words, which many times of purpose be so craftily put in and placed, that the bands can never be so sure nor so strong, but they will find some hole open to creep out at, and to break both league and truth. The which crafty dealing, yea, the which fraud and deceit, if they should know it to be practised among private men in their bargains and contracts, they would incontinent cry out at it with an open mouth and a sour countenance, as an offence most detestable, and worthy to be punished with a shameful death ; yea, even very they that advance themselves authors of like counsel given to princes. Wherefore it may well be thought, either that all justice is but a base and a low virtue, and which avaleth[1] itself far under the high dignity of kings, or, at the leastwise, that there be two justices, the one meet for the inferior sort of people, going afoot and creeping low by the ground, and bound down on every side with many bands, because it shall not run at rovers.[2] The other a princely virtue, which like as it is of much higher majesty

---

[1] *avaleth.* Debaseth.
[2] *run at rovers.* Run wild.

than the other poor justice, so also it is of much
more liberty, as to the which nothing is unlawful
that it lusteth after.

These manners of princes (as I said) which be
there so evil keepers of leagues, cause the Utopians,
as I suppose, to make no leagues at all, which
perchance would change their mind if they lived
here. Howbeit they think that though leagues be
never so faithfully observed and kept, yet the custom
of making leagues was very evil begun. For this
causeth men (as though nations which be separate
asunder, by the space of a little hill or a river, were
coupled together by no society or bond of nature[1])
to think themselves born adversaries and enemies

[1] *bond of nature*. The noble sentiments that conclude this
chapter are representative of the humanists and find many
an echo in Erasmus and his correspondents. I owe the
following note to Mr. R. O'Sullivan.

'Here we have a statement of "the good character of
natural man" by Thomas More in direct contradiction to
the contemporary teaching of Luther that the nature of man
is utterly depraved.

'The teaching of Thomas More is a restatement of the
teaching of St. Thomas Aquinas (*Summa Contra Gentes*,
Book III, Chapter CXVII, and elsewhere) and is in line
with the teaching of Erasmus and of Franciscus di Vittoria.
It is also in line with the teaching of the modern anthro-
pologists, e.g. Professor Elliot Smith in his book *On Human
History* and in two letters to *The Times* newspaper of
November 13, 1928, and November 15, 1929.

· The teaching of Luther is also the teaching of Hobbes
and of modern politics with its consequent exaltation of the
State and the transformation of Christendom into an armed
camp of hostile States.

'There are interesting passages with long extracts from
More and Erasmus in the work by Professor James Brown
Scott, the President of the International Law Association
of America on *The Spanish Origin of International Law*.'

one to another, and that it were lawful for the one
to seek the death and destruction of the other, if
leagues were not. Yea, and that after the leagues
be accorded, friendship doth not grow and increase,
but the licence of robbing and stealing doth still
remain, as farforth as for lack of foresight and
advisement in writing the words of the league, any
sentence or clause to the contrary is not therein
sufficiently comprehended.

But they be of a contrary opinion. That is, that
no man ought to be counted an enemy, which hath
done no injury. And that the fellowship of nature
is a strong league ; and that men be better and more
surely knit together by love and benevolence than
by covenants of leagues ; by hearty affection of
mind than by words.

OF WARFARE

WAR or battle as a thing very beastly, and yet to no kind of beasts in so much use as to man, they do detest and abhor. And contrary to the custom almost of all other nations, they count nothing so much against glory, as glory gotten in war. And therefore though they do daily practise and exercise themselves in the discipline of war, and not only the men, but also the women upon certain appointed days, lest they should be to seek in the feat of arms, if need should require, yet they never go to battle, but either in the defence of their own country, or to drive out of their friends' land the enemies that have invaded it, or by their power to deliver from the yoke and bondage of tyranny some people that be therewith oppressed. Which thing they do of mere pity and compassion.

Howbeit they send help to their friends not ever in their defence, but sometimes also to requite and revenge injuries before to them done. But this they do not unless their counsel and advice in the matter be asked whiles it is yet new and fresh. For if they find the cause probable, and if the contrary part will not restore again such things as be of them justly demanded, then they be the chief authors and makers of the war. Which they do not only as oft as by inroads and invasions of soldiers preys and booties be driven away, but then also much more

mortally when their friends' merchants in any land,
either under the pretence of unjust laws, or else by
the wresting and wrong understanding of good
laws, do sustain an unjust accusation under the
colour of justice.

Neither the battle which the Utopians fought for
the Nephelogetes[1] against the Alaopolitanes a little
before our time was made for any other cause, but
that the Nephelogete merchantmen, as the Utopians
thought, suffered wrong of the Alaopolitanes, under
the pretence of right. But whether it were right or
wrong, it was with so cruel and mortal war revenged, the countries round about joining their
help and power to the puissance and malice of both
parties, that most flourishing and wealthy peoples,
being some of them shrewdly shaken, and some of
them sharply beaten, the mischiefs were not finished
nor ended, until the Alaopolitanes at the last were
yielded up as bondmen into the jurisdiction of the
Nephelogetes. For the Utopians fought not this
war for themselves. And yet the Nephelogetes
before the war, when the Alaopolitanes flourished
in wealth, were nothing to be compared with them.

So eagerly the Utopians prosecute the injuries
done to their friends ; yea, in money matters, and

---

[1] *Nephelogetes and Alaopolitanes.* Fancy names from the
Greek, νεφέλη, a cloud, ἀλαός, blind, and πόλις, city.
It must be rarely, if ever, that some of the just grounds for
war enumerated by Hythloday, have not been invoked by
those who have begun hostilities. St. Thomas Aquinas
(II^a–II^{ae}, Q. xl, a. 1) quotes with approval St. Augustine's
summary of the conditions for a just war : ' Just wars are
usually defined as those which avenge injuries, if a nation
or a state . . . has either neglected to punish the evil deeds
of its citizens or to restore ill-gotten goods.'

not their own likewise. For if they by covin or guile be wiped beside[1] their goods, so that no violence be done to their bodies, they wreak their anger by abstaining from occupying with that nation until they have made satisfaction.

Not for because they set less store by their own citizens than by their friends, but that they take the loss of their friends' money more heavily than the loss of their own. Because that their friends' merchantmen, for as much as that they lose is their own private goods, sustain great damage by the loss. But their own citizens lose nothing but of the common goods, and of that which was at home plentiful and almost superfluous, else had it not been sent forth. Therefore no man feeleth the loss. And for this cause they think it too cruel an act to revenge that loss with the death of many, the incommodity of the which loss no man feeleth neither in his life, nor yet in his living.

But if it chance that any of their men in any other country be maimed or killed, whether it be done by a common or a private counsel, knowing and trying out the truth of the matter by their ambassadors, unless the offenders be rendered unto them in recompense of the injury, they will not be appeased, but incontinent they proclaim war against them. The offenders yielded, they punish either with death or with bondage.

They be not only sorry, but also ashamed to achieve the victory with bloodshed, counting it great folly to buy precious wares too dear. They rejoice and avaunt themselves if they vanquish and oppress their enemies by craft and deceit.

---

[1] *wiped beside.* Cheated of.

And for that act they make a general triumph, and
as if the matter were manfully handled, they set up
a pillar of stone in the place where they so vanquished their enemies, in token of the victory.
For then they glory, then they boast and crack
that they have played the men indeed, when they
have so overcome, as no other living creature but
only man could, that is to say, by the might and
puissance of wit. For with bodily strength (say
they) bears, lions, boars, wolves, dogs, and other
wild beasts do fight. And as the most part of them
do pass us in strength and fierce courage, so in wit
and reason we be much stronger than they all.

Their chief and principal purpose in war is to
obtain that thing which, if they had before obtained,
they would not have moved battle. But if that be
not possible, they take so cruel vengeance of them
which be in the fault, that ever after they be afraid
to do the like. This is their chief and principal
intent, which they immediately and first of all
prosecute and set forward. But yet so, that they be
more circumspect in avoiding and eschewing
jeopardies, than they be desirous of praise and
renown. Therefore immediately after that war is
once solemnly denounced, they procure many
proclamations signed with their own common
seal to be set up privily at one time in their
enemies' land, in places most frequented. In these
proclamations they promise great rewards to him
that will kill their enemies' prince, and somewhat
less gifts, but them very great also, for every head
of them whose names be in the said proclamations
contained. They be those whom they count their
chief adversaries, next unto the prince. Whatso-

ever is prescribed unto him that killeth any of the proclaimed persons, that is doubled to him that bringeth any of the same to them alive ; yea, and to the proclaimed persons themselves, if they will change their minds and come in to them, taking their parts, they proffer the same great rewards with pardon, and surety of their lives.

Therefore it quickly cometh to pass that their enemies have all other men in suspicion, and be unfaithful and mistrusting among themselves one to another, living in great fear, and in no less jeopardy. For it is well known that divers times the most part of them (and especially the prince himself) hath been betrayed of them in whom they put their most hope and trust. So that there is no manner of act nor deed that gifts and rewards do not enforce men unto. And in rewards they keep no measure. But remembering and considering into how great hazard and jeopardy they call them, endeavour themselves to recompense the greatness of the danger with like great benefits. And therefore they promise not only wonderful great abundance of gold, but also lands of great revenues lying in most safe places among their friends. And their promises they perform faithfully without any fraud or covin.

This custom of buying and selling adversaries among other people is disallowed, as a cruel act of a base and a cowardish mind. But they in this behalf think themselves much praiseworthy, as who like wise men by this means despatch great wars without any battle or skirmish. Yea, they count it also a deed of pity and mercy, because that by the death of a few offenders the lives of a great number

of innocents, as well of their own men as also of
their enemies, be ransomed and saved, which in
fighting should have been slain. For they do no
less pity the base and common sort of their enemies'
people than they do their own ; knowing that they
be driven and enforced to war against their wills by
the furious madness of their princes and heads.

If by none of these means the matter go forward
as they would have it, then they procure occasions
of debate[1] and dissension to be spread among their
enemies. As by bringing the prince's brother,
or some of the noblemen in hope to obtain the
kingdom. If this way prevail not, then they raise
up the people that be next neighbours and borderers
to their enemies, and them they set in their necks[2]
under the colour of some old title of right, such as
kings do never lack. To them they promise their
help and aid in their war. And as for money they
give them abundance, but of their own citizens they
send to them few or none. Whom they make so
much of, and love so entirely, that they would not
be willing to change any of them for their adversaries' prince. But their gold and silver, because

---

[1] *occasions of debate.* More is satirising the practices he
saw around him. As Professor Brewer writes : ' A practice
which seems the more odious in these upright and wise
Utopians was tenfold more unjustifiable in those who,
professing the doctrines of Christ, never scrupled to employ
the same means against their own enemies. Were the
intrigues of Henry VIII and his minister Dacre against
Scotland more moral than these ? Were not their attempts
to sow treason and disaffection among the Scotch lords an
exact exemplification of this Utopian policy ? ' (*Reign of
Henry VIII*, Vol. 1, p. 289.)

[2] *set in their necks.* Set on them.

they keep it all for this only purpose, they lay it
out frankly and freely ; as who should live even
as wealthy, if they had bestowed it every penny.
Yea and besides their riches which they keep at
home, they have also an infinite treasure abroad, by
reason that (as I said before) many nations be in
their debt. Therefore they hire soldiers out of all
countries and send them to battle ; but chiefly of the
Zapoletes.[1]

This people is 500 miles from Utopia eastward.
They be hideous, savage, and fierce, dwelling in
wild woods and high mountains, where they were
bred and brought up. They be of a hard nature,
able to abide and sustain heat, cold, and labour,
abhorring from all delicate dainties, occupying no
husbandry nor tillage of the ground, homely and
rude both in building of their houses and in their
apparel, given unto no goodness, but only to the
breeding and bringing up of cattle. The most
part of their living is by hunting and stealing. They
be born only to war, which they diligently and
earnestly seek for. And when they have gotten it,
they be wondrous glad thereof. They go forth
of their country in great companies together, and
whosoever lacketh soldiers, there they proffer their
service for small wages. This is only the craft they
have to get their living by. They maintain their life
by seeking their death. For them whom with they

[1] *Zapoletes*. Derived by More, as Dr. Lupton points out,
from ζα, intensive, and πωλεῖν, to sell, i.e. ready to sell
their services as mercenaries. A marginal note in the edition
of 1517 may be translated, ' A race not unlike the Swiss.'
They seem at that time fully to have deserved the unpleasant
character here ascribed to them.

be in wages they fight hardly, fiercely, and faithfully. But they bind themselves for no certain time. But upon this condition they enter into bonds, that the next day they will take part with the other side for greater wages, and the next day after that, they will be ready to come back again for a little more money. There be few wars thereaway, wherein is not a great number of them in both parties. Therefore it daily chanceth that any kinsfolk which were hired together on one part, and there very friendly and familiarly used themselves one with another, shortly after being separate in contrary parts, run one against another enviously and fiercely, and forgetting both kindred and friendship, thrust their swords one in another. And that for none other cause, but that they be hired of contrary princes for a little money. Which they do so highly regard and esteem, that they will easily be provoked to change parts for a halfpenny more wages by the day. So quickly they have taken a smack in covetousness. Which for all that is to them no profit. For that they get by fighting, immediately they spend unthriftily and wretchedly in riot.

This people fighteth for the Utopians against all nations, because they give them greater wages than any other nation will. For the Utopians like as they seek good men to use well, so they seek these evil and vicious men to abuse. Whom, when need requireth, with promises of great rewards they put forth into great jeopardies. From whence the most part of them never cometh again to ask their rewards. But to them that remain alive they pay that which they promised faithfully, that they may be the more willing to put themselves in like danger

another time.   Nor the Utopians pass not how many
of them they bring to destruction.   For they believe
that they should do a very good deed for all man-
kind, if they could rid out of the world all the foul
stinking den of that most wicked and cursed people.

Next unto these they use the soldiers of them for
whom they fight.   And then the help of their other
friends.   And last of all, they join to their own
citizens.   Among whom they give to one of tried
virtue and prowess the rule, governance, and con-
duction of the whole army.   Under him they
appoint two others, which, while he is safe, be
both private and out of office.   But if he be taken or
slain, the one of the other two succeedeth him, as
it were by inheritance.   And if the second miscarry,
then the third taketh his room, lest that (as the
chance of battle is uncertain and doubtful) the
jeopardy or death of the captain should bring
the whole army in hazard.

They choose soldiers, out of every city those
which put forth themselves willingly.   For they
thrust no man forth into war against his will.
Because they believe, if any man be fearful and
faint-hearted of nature, he will not only do no manful and hardy act himself, but also be occasion of
cowardness to his fellows.[1]   But if any battle be
made against their own country, then they put
these cowards (so that they be strong bodied) in
ships among other bold-hearted men.   Or else
they dispose them upon the walls, from whence

[1] *to his fellows.*   So also in the Mosaic Law : ' What man
is there that is fearful and faint-hearted ?   Let him go and
return to his house, lest he make the hearts of his brethren
to fear, as he himself is possessed with fear.'   (*Deut*. xx, 8.)

they may not fly. Thus what for shame that their
enemies be at hand, and what for because they be
without hope of running away, they forget all fear.
And many times extreme necessity turneth cowardness into prowess and manliness.

But as none of them is thrust forth of his country
into war against his will, so women that be willing
to accompany their husbands in times of war be
not prohibited or letted. Yea, they provoke and
exhort them to it with praises. And in set field
the wives do stand every one by their own husband's
side. Also every man is compassed next about
with his own children, kinsfolks, and alliance,
that they, whom nature chiefly moveth to mutual
succour, thus standing together, may help one
another. It is a great reproach and dishonesty for
the husband to come home without his wife, or
the wife without her husband, or the son without
his father. And therefore if the other part stick
so hard by it that the battle come to their hands,
it is fought with great slaughter and bloodshed,
even to the utter destruction of both parts. For as
they make all the means and shifts that may be to
keep themselves from the necessity of fighting, or
that they may despatch the battle by their hired
soldiers ; so when there is no remedy, but that
they must needs fight themselves, then they do as
courageously fall to it, as before, whilst they might,
they did wisely avoid and refuse it. Nor they be
not most fierce at the first brunt. But in continuance by little and little their fierce courage
increaseth, with so stubborn and obstinate minds,
that they will rather die than give back an inch.
For that surety of living which every man hath at

home being joined with no careful anxiety or remembrance how their posterity shall live after them (for this pensiveness oftentimes breaketh and abateth courageous stomachs), maketh them stout and hardy, and disdainful to be conquered. Moreover their knowledge in chivalry and feats of arms putteth them in a good hope. Finally the wholesome and virtuous opinions, wherein they were brought up even from their childhood, partly through learning, and partly through the good ordinances and laws of their weal public, augment and increase their manful courage. By reason whereof they neither set so little store by their lives, that they will rashly and unadvisedly cast them away ; nor they be not so far in lewd and fond love therewith, that they will shamefully covet to keep them, when honesty biddeth leave them.

When the battle is hottest and in all places most fierce and fervent, a band of chosen and picked young men, which be sworn to live and die together, take upon them to destroy their adversaries' captain, whom they invade, now with privy wiles, now by open strength. At him they strike both near and far off. He is assailed with a long and a continual assault, fresh men still coming in the wearied men's places. And seldom it chanceth (unless he save himself by flying) that he is not either slain, or else taken prisoner, and yielded to his enemies alive.

If they win the field, they persecute not their enemies with the violent rage of slaughter. For they had rather take them alive than kill them. Neither they do so follow the chase and pursuit of their enemies, but they leave behind them one part

of their host in battle array under their standards.
In so much that if all their whole army be discom-
fited and overcome saving the rearward, and that
they therewith achieve the victory, then they had
rather let all their enemies escape than to follow
them out of array. For they remember it hath
chanced unto themselves more than once; the
whole power and strength of their host being
vanquished and put to flight, whilst their enemies
rejoicing in the victory have persecuted them flying
some one way and some another, a small company
of their men lying in an ambush, there ready at all
occasions, have suddenly risen upon them thus
dispersed and scattered out of array, and through
presumption of safety unadvisedly pursuing the
chase; and have incontinent changed the fortune
of the whole battle, and, spite of their teeth[1] wresting
out of their hands the sure and undoubted victory,
being a little before conquered, have for their part
conquered the conquerors.

It is hard to say whether they be craftier in laying
an ambush, or wittier in avoiding the same. You
would think they intend to fly, when they mean
nothing less. And contrariwise when they go
about that purpose, you would believe it were the
least part of their thought. For if they perceive
themselves either overmatched in number, or closed
in too narrow a place, then they remove their
camp either in the night season with silence, or by
some policy they deceive their enemies, or in the
day-time they retire back so softly,[2] that it is no less

---

[1] *spite of their teeth.* Despite their best efforts.
[2] *softly.* Gradually. The Latin adds 'keeping such good
formation.'

jeopardy to meddle with them when they give back than when they press on.

They fence and fortify their camp surely with a deep and a broad trench. The earth thereof is cast inward. Nor they do not set drudges and slaves awork about it. It is done by the hands of the soldiers themselves. All the whole army worketh upon it, except them that keep watch and ward in harness before the trench for sudden adventures. Therefore by the labour of so many a large trench closing in a great compass of ground is made in less time than any man would believe.

Their armour or harness which they wear is sure and strong to receive strokes, and handsome[1] for all movings and gestures of the body, insomuch that it is not unwieldy to swim in. For in the discipline of their warfare among other feats they learn to swim in harness. Their weapons be arrows aloof, which they shoot both strongly and surely, not only footmen, but also horsemen. At hand strokes they use not swords but pole-axes, which be mortal, as well in sharpness as in weight, both for foins[2] and down strokes. Engines for war they devise and invent wondrous wittily. Which when they be made they keep very secret, lest if they should be known before need require, they should be but laughed at and serve to no purpose. But in making them, hereunto they have chief respect, that they be both easy to be carried and handsome to be moved and turned about.

Truce taken with their enemies for a short time they do so firmly and faithfully keep, that they will

---

[1] *handsome.* The Latin is *habiles*, suitable, convenient.
[2] *foins.* Thrusts.

not break it; no not though they be thereunto
provoked. They do not waste nor destroy their
enemies' land with foragings, nor they burn not
up their corn. Yea, they save it as much as may
be from being overrun and trodden down either
with men or horses, thinking that it groweth for
their own use and profit.

They hurt no man that is unarmed, unless he
be a spy. All cities that be yielded unto them, they
defend. And such as they win by force of assault,
they neither despoil nor sack, but them that with-
stood and dissuaded the yielding up of the same,
they put to death, the other soldiers they punish
with bondage. All the weak multitude they leave
untouched. If they know that any citizens coun-
selled to yield and render up the city, to them they
give part of the condemned men's goods. The
residue they distribute and give freely among them
whose help they had in the same war. For none
of themselves taketh any portion of the prey.

But when the battle is finished and ended, they
put their friends to never a penny cost of all the
charges that they were at, but lay it upon their
necks that be conquered. Them they burden with
the whole charge of their expenses, which they
demand of them partly in money to be kept for
like use of battle, and partly in lands of great
revenues to be paid unto them yearly for ever.
Such revenues they have now in many countries,
which by little and little rising of divers and sundry
causes be increased above seven hundred thousand
ducats by the year. Thither they send forth some
of their citizens as lieutenants, to live there
sumptuously like men of honour and renown.

And yet this notwithstanding much money is saved, which cometh to the common treasury; unless it so chance that they had rather trust the country with the money. Which many times they do so long, until they have need to occupy it. And it seldom happeneth that they demand all. Of these lands they assign part unto them which at their request and exhortation put themselves in such jeopardies as I spake of before.

If any prince stir up war against them, intending to invade their land, they meet him incontinent out of their own borders with great power and strength. For they never lightly make war in their own country. Nor they be never brought into so extreme necessity as to take help out of foreign lands into their own island.

OF THE RELIGIONS IN UTOPIA

THERE be divers kinds of religion not only in sundry parts of the island, but also in divers places of every city. Some worship for God the sun ; some the moon ;[1] some, some other of the planets. There be that give worship to a man[2] that was once of excellent virtue or of famous glory, not only as God, but also as the chiefest and highest God. But the most and the wisest part (rejecting all these) believe that there is a certain godly power[3] unknown, everlasting, incom-

---

[1] *. . . the sun . . . the moon.* Perhaps More had in mind *Wisdom* xiii, 1, 2 : ' But all men are vain in whom there is not the knowledge of God : . . . but have imagined either the fire, or the wind, or the swift air, or the circle of the stars, or the great water, or the sun and moon, to be the gods that rule the world.' See also *De Civitate Dei*, Book VII, Chapter XVI.

[2] *. . . a man.* The Latin *quispiam* is indefinite, i.e. ' any man.'

[3] *. . . a certain godly power.* Burnet's translation brings out more clearly the emphatically-placed *unum*, ' one eternal, invisible, infinite, and incomprehensible Deity.' These attributes of God, known to us by human reason, are treated of very fully by St. Thomas Aquinas in the opening questions of the *Summa*. Or More was perhaps re-echoing such words as ' the Lord of lords, who only hath immortality, and inhabiteth light inaccessible, whom no man hath seen, nor can see, to whom be honour and empire everlasting. Amen.' (1 *Tim.* vi, 16.)

prehensible, inexplicable, far above the capacity and reach of man's wit, dispersed throughout all the world, not in bigness, but in virtue and power. Him they call the father of all. To him alone they attribute the beginnings, the increasings, the proceedings, the changes, and the ends of all things. Neither they give any divine honours to any other than to him.

Yea, all the other also, though they be in divers opinions, yet in this point they agree altogether with the wisest sort, in believing that there is one chief and principal God, the maker and ruler of the whole world, whom they all commonly in their country language call Mithra.[1] But in this they disagree, that among some he is counted one, and among some another. For every one of them, whatsoever that is which he taketh for the chief god, thinketh it to be the very same nature, to whose only divine might and majesty the sum and sovereignty of all things by the consent of all people is attributed and given.

Howbeit they all begin by little and little to forsake and fall from this variety of superstitions, and to agree together in that religion[2] which seemeth by reason to pass and excel the residue. And it is not to be doubted, but all the other would long ago have been abolished, but that whatsoever unprosperous thing happened to any of them, as

[1] . . . *Mithra.* The Persian sun-god whose worship was widely diffused in the Roman Empire. Above (p. 159) More has said that the Utopian language is ‘ not much unlike the Persian tongue.’

[2] . . . *that religion*, i.e. that which he has just before ascribed to ‘ the most and the wisest part.’

he was minded to change his religion, the fearfulness of people did take it, not as a thing coming by chance, but as sent from God out of heaven. As though the God, whose honour he was forsaking would revenge[1] that wicked purpose against him.

But after they heard us speak of the name of Christ, of His doctrine, laws, miracles, and of the no less wonderful constancy of so many martyrs, whose blood[2] willingly shed brought a great number of nations throughout all parts of the world into their sect, you will not believe with how glad minds they agreed unto the same; whether it were by the secret inspiration of God, or else for that they thought it nighest unto that opinion,[3] which among them is counted the chiefest. Howbeit I think this was no small help and furtherance in the matter, that they heard us say, that Christ instituted[4] among His all things common, and that

[1] . . . *as though God . . . would revenge.* It was a chief purpose of St. Augustine in *De Civitate Dei* to refute the superstition that misfortunes had fallen upon Rome because it had turned away from the pagan gods.

[2] . . . *whose blood.* Cf. Tertullian's words : *Semen est sanguis Christianorum.* 'The seed is the blood of the Christians.'

[3] . . . *that opinion.* See above, p. 194, n. 3.

[4] . . . *instituted* does not correctly translate *Christo placuisse.* The meaning is that Christ approved of a community of life. The reference may be to the Apostles living in common with Our Lord, or to the early Christians of whom it is said : ' All they that believed were together, and had all things common.' (*Acts* ii, 44.) The marginal note, *coenobia,* recalls the monasteries, so prominent a feature in historical Christianity, where the common life was practised. Much that is ascribed to the Utopians clearly is based upon

the same community doth yet remain amongst the rightest Christian companies. Verily, howsoever it came to pass, many of them consented together in our religion, and were washed in the holy water of baptism.

But because among us four (for no more of us was left alive, two of our company being dead) there was no priest, which I am right sorry for, they being entered[1] and instructed in all other points of our religion, lack only those sacraments which here none but priests do minister. Howbeit they understand and perceive them, and be very desirous of the same. Yea, they reason and dispute the matter earnestly among themselves, whether without the sending of a Christian bishop, one chosen out of their own people may receive the order of priesthood.[2] And truly they were minded to choose one. But at my departure from them they had chosen none.

They also which do not agree to Christ's religion

monastic usages. The monastic life is based upon the observance of the counsels of poverty, chastity, and obedience, so earnestly recommended by Our Lord, and therefore is rightly said here to have His approval. (See also below, p. 226).

[1] . . . *being entered*. *Ceteris initiati*, etc., means that they had received the Sacraments which can be given in certain cases without the ministry of a priest, i.e. Baptism which in a case of necessity can be conferred by anyone, and Marriage which the two spouses confer upon each other, though normally a priest—the Church's official representative—must be present.

[2] . . . *the order of priesthood*. More uses the theological term *the character of the priesthood*. The question is one that might be expected to be discussed in such an age of new discoveries, but it admits of a negative answer alone. See More's words quoted below, p. 210 n.

fear no man from it, nor speak against any man
that hath received it. Saving that one of our
company in my presence was sharply punished.
He as soon as he was baptised, began against our
wills, with more earnest affection than wisdom, to
reason of Christ's religion, and began to wax so
hot in his matter, that he did not only prefer our
religion before all other, but also did utterly despise
and condemn all other, calling them profane, and
the followers of them wicked and devilish,[1] and
the children of everlasting damnation. When he had
thus long reasoned the matter, they laid hold on
him, accused him, and condemned him into exile,
not as a despiser of religion, but as a seditious
person, and a raiser up of dissension among the
people. For this is one of the ancientest laws
among them : that no man shall be blamed for
reasoning[2] in the maintenance of his own religion.

For King Utopus, even at the first beginning,
hearing that the inhabitants of the land were before
his coming thither, at continual dissension and strife
among themselves for their religions ; perceiving
also that this common dissension (whilst every
several sect took several parts in fighting for their
country) was the only occasion of his conquest
over them all, as soon as he had gotten the victory,

[1] . . . *wicked and devilish*. Robinson's picturesque version
of the literal *impios ac sacrilegos*, ' impious and sacrilegious.'

[2] . . . *blamed for reasoning*. The original says nothing here
of ' reasoning,' though that matter is dealt with in the next
section. *Ne sua cuiquam religio fraudi sit* means ' that no
man's religion should be a (social or civil) disability to him.'
This is qualified by what More says below, unless one
should prefer to say that More does not put irreligion on
an equality with religion.

first of all he made a decree, that it should be lawful for every man to favour and follow what religion he would, and that he might do the best he could to bring others to his opinion, so that he did it peaceably, gently, quietly, and soberly, without hasty and contentious rebuking and inveighing against others. If he could not by fair and gentle speech induce them unto his opinion, yet he should use no kind of violence, and refrain from displeasant and seditious words. To him that would vehemently and fervently in this cause strive and contend was decreed banishment or bondage.

This law did King Utopus make not only for the maintenance of peace, which he saw through continual contention and mortal hatred utterly extinguished, but also because he thought this decree should make for the furtherance of religion. Whereof he durst define and determine nothing unadvisedly, as doubting whether God desiring manifold and divers sorts of honour, would inspire sundry men with sundry kinds of religion. And this surely he thought a very unmeet and foolish thing, and a point of arrogant presumption, to compel all others by violence and threatenings to agree to the same that thou believest to be true.[1]

[1] . . . *believest to be true.* More's words are in full accord with the teaching of St. Thomas Aquinas who in answer to the question ' Whether infidels are to be brought by force to the faith ' pens these golden words : ' Such infidels as have never received the faith, like pagans and Jews, are to be subjected to no kind of force to make them believe, for faith is a matter of free will ; but the faithful should, if they are able, force them not to hinder the spread of the faith by either blasphemies, or seduction, or by open persecutions.' (II^a–II^{ae}, Q. 10, a. 8.) When it is urged, as often

Furthermore, though there be one religion which
alone is true, and all others vain and superstitious

it has been, that More's own practice did not accord with
this principle, it is forgotten that heretics stand on an entirely
different footing. As St. Thomas says in the same place :
' Those infidels however, who once received the faith and
professed it, like heretics and apostates, are to be forced to
fulfil what they have promised, and to hold to what they
have once undertaken.' The Utopians had never had the
light of revelation, but the heretics of St. Thomas More's
day were rebels not only against the Church, but against
the established order of society. They are put in the very
lowest company in the epitaph he composed for himself,
' not unpopular with the citizens, but to thieves, murderers,
and heretics grievous.' More found his worst forebodings
confirmed when he heard of the horrors of the sack of
Rome in 1527 by the Lutheran soldiery. (He describes them
in his *Dialogue*, E. W., p. 258.) Sir James Mackintosh
speaks of the ' blood-stained hands of the boors of Saxony,
and of the ferocious fanatics of Munster.' (*Life of More*,
p. 98.) More defends the civil laws against heresy, even in
extreme cases the death penalty, on the ground of the
State's right of self-defence. ' The violent cruelty first used
by the heretics themselves against good Catholic folk drove
good princes thereto, for preservation not of the faith only,
but also of the peace among their people ' (E. W., p. 275).
Tyndale knows full well, he says, that ' his own fellows,
the heretics of his own sect, rose there (i.e. in Germany)
and robbed and burned and killed, not one naughty knave
or two in a town, as good kings and princes do these horrible
and incorrigible heretics, and yet sometimes scant once in
ten years, and in some good town not once in ten score
years, but whole goodly monasteries they burned up and
destroyed, and somewhere all the churches almost through
the whole country, robbed, spoiled, and bare away all that
ever they found, despited the saints' images, relics, the
crucifix, and the Blessed Sacrament, robbed, maimed, and
murdered many good virtuous people.' (E. W., p. 570.)

As Chancellor More administered the laws against heresy
justly but not harshly. Foxe has preserved some of the wild

yet did he well foresee (so that the matter were
handled with reason[1] and sober modesty) that the
truth of the own power would at the last issue out
and come to light. But if contention and debate
in that behalf should continually be used, as the
worst men be most obstinate and stubborn, and
in their evil opinion most constant, he perceived
that then the best and holiest religion would be
trodden underfoot and destroyed by most vain
superstitions, even as good corn is by thorns and
weeds overgrown and choked.

stories the heretics invented about him, but More deals
with them in his *Apology* (E. W., p. 902), and later research
has tended to substantiate his defence and show the untrust-
worthiness of Foxe. See the full treatment in Bridgett,
Chapter XIV, and in Chambers (p. 274).

[1] . . . *handled with reason.* It has been the constant teaching
of the Church from the days of St. Paul that the truths of
natural religion, the existence of God our Maker and our
Judge, with the complementary truth of man's after-life,
can be learned by human reason without the aid of revelation.
Thus the Vatican Council teaches : ' God, the beginning
and the end of all things, can by the natural light of human
reason be known with certainty from the works of creation,
" for the invisible things of Him, from the creation of the
world, are clearly seen, being understood by the things that
are made " (*Rom.* i, 20).' (*Cap* 2, *De Revelatione*.) Moreover
the Catholic Church has evidences of her divine authority,
viz. her characteristic marks of unity, catholicity, etc., which
are entirely within the competence of human reason and
appeal to be judged impartially by it. Throughout it is
essential to remember that the Utopians were pagans who
had never received God's revelation. After, however,
reason has established the credentials of the Catholic Church,
it has no place in discovering the content of her teaching.
Its task is now the negative one of showing that there is no
unfitness nor inconsistency in the various parts of the divine
revelation, and of removing difficulties.

Therefore all this matter he left undiscussed, and
gave to every man free liberty and choice to believe
what he would; saving that he earnestly and
straightly charged[1] them, that no man should
conceive so vile and base an opinion of the dignity
of man's nature as to think that the souls do die
and perish with the body, or that the world runneth
at all adventures governed by no divine providence.
And therefore they believe that after this life vices
be extremely punished and virtues bountifully
rewarded. Him that is of a contrary opinion they
count not in the number of men, as one that hath
avaled[2] the high nature of his soul to the vileness
of brute beasts' bodies : much less in the number
of their citizens, whose laws and ordinances, if it
were not for fear, he would nothing at all esteem.
For you may be sure that he will study either with
craft privily to mock, or else violently to break the
common laws of his country, in whom remaineth
no further fear than of the laws, nor no further
hope than of the body. Wherefore, he that is thus
minded is deprived of all honours, excluded from
all offices, and reject from all common administra-
tions in the weal public. And thus he is of all
sorts despised, as of an unprofitable, and of a base
and vile nature. Howbeit they put him to no
punishment,[3] because they be persuaded that it is

[1] . . . *straitly charged*. *Sancte ac severe vetuit ne* means rather
' He most strictly and severely forbade anyone to conceive,
etc.' The two truths of the future life and divine providence
are the fundamental truths of natural religion which can be
known without the aid of revelation (see previous note).

[2] *avaled*. Debased.

[3] . . . *no punishment*. The disqualifications are severe
enough but they are not bodily punishment, which is the
meaning of *supplicium*.

in no man's power to believe what he list. No nor they constrain him not with threatenings to dissemble his mind, and show countenance contrary to his thought. For deceit and falsehood and all manners of lies, as next unto fraud, they do marvellously detest and abhor. But they suffer him not to dispute in his opinion, and that only[1] among the common people. For else apart among the priests and men of gravity they do not only suffer, but also exhort him to dispute and argue, hoping that at the last that madness will give place to reason.

There be also other, and of them no small number, which be not forbidden to speak their minds, as grounding their opinion upon some reason, being in their living neither evil nor vicious. Their heresy is much contrary to the other. For they believe that the souls of brute beasts be immortal and everlasting. But nothing to be compared with ours in dignity, neither ordained nor predestinate to like felicity.

For all they believe certainly and surely that man's bliss shall be so great, that they do mourn and lament every man's sickness, but no man's death, unless it be one whom they see depart from his life carefully and against his will. For this they take for a very evil token, as though the soul being in despair and vexed in conscience, through some privy and secret forefeeling of the punishment now at hand, were afraid to depart. And they think he shall not be welcome to God, which, when he is called, runneth not to Him

[1] . . . *and that only*, i.e. disputing is forbidden only among the common people.

gladly,[1] but is drawn by force and sore against his
will. They, therefore, that see this kind of death,
do abhor it, and them that so die they bury with
sorrow and silence. And when they have prayed
God to be merciful to the soul, and mercifully to
pardon the infirmities thereof, they cover the dead
corpse with earth.

Contrariwise all that depart merely and full of
good hope, for them no man mourneth, but
followeth the hearse with joyful singing, com-
mending the souls to God with great affection.
And at the last, not with mourning sorrow, but
with a great reverence they burn the bodies. And
in the same place they set up a pillar of stone with
the dead man's titles therein graved. When they
be come home they rehearse his virtuous manners
and his good deeds. But no part of his life is so
oft or gladly talked of as his merry death.

[1] . . . *gladly.* A favourite thought with More. He will
have known St. Gregory's words, 'He is not willing to open
to the Judge who knocks, who fears to leave the body and
dreads to see as his Judge Him whom his conscience tells
him he has despised. But he who is without anxiety for
his past deeds and firm in hope, opens at once to Him who
knocks, for he awaits his Judge with joy, and when the
moment of death draws nigh, he is filled with gladness in
the hope of a glorious reward.'

He expresses the same thought in his *Dialogue of Comfort*,
p. 47.

No doubt More wishes to point out, by contrast, the
insincerity of many Christians who dread the future life.
At any rate he practised what he preached as can be seen in
Roper's narrative of his martyrdom.

Why More should have assigned earth-burial to the bad
and cremation to the good it is impossible to say. Earth-
burial was the Christian tradition, adopted from the Jews,
whereas cremation was the custom of the pagan Romans,
adopted from the Greeks.

They think that this remembrance of the virtue and goodness of the dead doth vehemently provoke and enforce the living to virtue. And that nothing can be more pleasant and acceptable to the dead. Whom they suppose to be present among them, when they talk of them, though to the dull and feeble eyesight of mortal men they be invisible. For it were an inconvenient thing that the blessed should not be at liberty to go whither they would. And it were a point of great unkindness in them to have utterly cast away the desire of visiting and seeing their friends, to whom they were in their lifetime joined by mutual love and amity. Which in good men after their death they count to be rather increased than diminished. They believe, therefore, that the dead be presently conversant among the quick, as beholders and witnesses[1] of all their words and deeds. Therefore they go more courageously to their business as having a trust and affiance in such overseers. And this same belief of the present conversation of their forefathers and ancestors among them, feareth them from all secret dishonesty.

They utterly despise and mock soothsayings and divinations of things to come by the flight or voices of birds, and all other divinations of vain superstition, which in other countries be in great observation. But they highly esteem and worship miracles[2] that come by no help of nature, as works

[1] . . . *witnesses.* Was More thinking of *Hebrews* xii, 1 : ' We also having so great a cloud of witnesses over us, etc.' ?

[2] . . . *vain superstition* . . . *miracles.* For a similar contrast Dr. Lupton quotes More's *Dialogue*, ' For that is a good mark between God's miracles and the devil's wonders. For

and witnesses of the present power of God. And
such they say do chance there very often. And
sometimes in great and doubtful matters, by
common intercession and prayers, they procure and
obtain them with a sure hope and confidence and a
steadfast belief.

They think that the contemplation of nature,
and the praise thereof coming, is to God a very
acceptable honour. Yet there be many so earnestly
bent and affectioned to religion, that they pass
nothing for learning, nor give their minds to any
knowledge of things. But idleness they utterly
forsake and eschew, thinking felicity after this life
to be gotten and obtained by busy labours and good
exercises. Some, therefore, of them attend upon
the sick, some amend highways, cleanse ditches,
repair bridges, dig turfs, gravel, and stones, fell
and cleave wood, bring wood, corn, and other
things into the cities in carts, and serve not only
in common works, but also in private labours as
servants, yea, more than bondmen. For whatsoever
unpleasant, hard, and vile work is anywhere, from
the which labour, loathsomeness, and desperation
doth frighten others, all that they take upon them
willingly and gladly, procuring quiet and rest to
others, remaining in continual work and labour
themselves, not upbraiding others therewith. They
neither reprove other men's lives nor glory in their

Christ and His saints have their miracles always tending to
fruit and profit. The devil and his witches and necromancers,
all their wonderful works draw to no fruitful end, but to a
fruitless ostentation and show, as it were a juggler that
would for a show before the people play masteries at a
feast.' (E. W., p. 1091.)

own. These men the more serviceable they behave themselves, the more they be honoured of all men.

Yet they be divided into two sects.[1] The one is of them that live single and chaste, abstaining not only from the company of women, but also from eating of flesh, and some of them from all manner of beasts. Which utterly rejecting the pleasures of this present life as hurtful, be all wholly set upon the desire of the life to come by watching and sweating, hoping shortly to obtain it, being in the mean season merry and lusty. The other sect is no less desirous of labour, but they embrace matrimony, not despising the solace thereof, thinking that they cannot be discharged of their bounden duties towards nature without labour and toil, nor towards their native country without procreation of children. They abstain from no pleasure that doth nothing hinder them from labour. They love the flesh of four-footed beasts, because they believe that by that meat they be made hardier and stronger to work. The Utopians count this sect the wiser, but the other the holier. Which in that they prefer single life before matrimony, and that sharp life before an easier life, if herein they grounded upon reason they would mock them. But now forasmuch as they say they be led to it by religion, they honour and worship them. And these be they whom in their language by a peculiar name they call

---

[1] ... *two sects*. In what follows More is perhaps recounting some of the considerations that weighed with him when, living in the London Charterhouse, he debated the matter of his vocation. He chose matrimony, but also a life free neither from severe labours, nor from asceticism. (*v.* Stapleton, pp. 9, 10.)

Buthrescas, the which word by interpretation signifieth to us men of religion or religious men.

They have priests of exceeding holiness, and therefore very few.[1] For there be but thirteen in every city according to the number of their churches, saving when they go forth to battle. For then seven of them go forth with the army, in whose stead so many new be made at home. But the other at their return home again re-enter every one into his own place, they that be above the number, until such time as they succeed into the places of the others at their dying, be in the mean season continually in company with the bishop.[2] For he is the chief head of them all.

They be chosen of the people, as the other magistrates be, by secret voices, for the avoiding of strife. After their election they be consecrated of

---

[1] . . . *therefore very few*. Obviously, for the best cannot but be few. Some commentators bid us notice here ' More's dislike of priests ' ! In his *Dialogue of* 1528 he repeats his desire for fewer, but better, priests. All would be well if the Church's laws were observed, but they are evaded; and as priests lack that ground of support (' title for ordination ') which the law requires they are forced to go a-begging, or live in a layman's house, ' so that every mean man must have a priest to wait upon his wife.' He claims that some of the bishops are of his mind in this matter Book III, Chapter XII).

In fact More's greatest friends were priests. Besides Erasmus, there were St. John Fisher, John Colet, Thomas Lupset, Cuthbert Tunstall, William Latimer, John Grocyn, Blessed Richard Reynolds, the Brigettine of Syon Abbey, and his own parish priest, Blessed John Larke.

[2] . . . *bishop*. *Pontificis*, i.e. high priest. One would not expect pagans to have bishops.

their own company. They be overseers of all divine matters, orderers of religions, and as it were judges and masters of manners. And it is a great dishonesty and shame to be rebuked or spoken to by any of them for dissolute and incontinent living. But as it is their office to give good exhortations and counsel, so is it the duty of the prince and the other magistrates to correct and punish offenders, saving that the priests whom they find exceeding vicious livers, them they excommunicate from having any interest in divine matters. And there is almost no punishment among them more feared. For they run in very great infamy, and be inwardly tormented with a secret fear of religion, and shall not long escape free with their bodies. For unless they by quick repentance approve the amendment of their lives to the priests, they be taken and punished[1] of the council as wicked and irreligious.

Both childhood and youth is instructed and taught of them. Nor they be not more diligent to instruct them in learning than in virtue and good manners. For they use with very great endeavour and diligence to put into the heads of their children, whilst they be yet tender and pliant, good opinions and profitable for the conservation of their weal public. Which, when they be once rooted in children, do remain with them all their life after, and be wondrous profitable for the defence and maintenance of the state of the commonwealth. Which never decayeth but through vices rising of evil opinions.

[1] . . . *taken and punished*. Note the close union of Church and State.

The priests, unless they be women¹ (for that kind

¹ . . . *women.* More is imagining a pagan community and
could have quoted many instances from pagan religions of
women priests. But to suggest as Seebohm does (*Oxford
Reformers*, p. 363) that More seriously considered that
women should be admitted to the Catholic priesthood is to
mistake the whole character of the *Utopia*. Tyndale reckoned
' every woman a priest, and as able to say Mass as ever was
St. Peter.' More's reply is devastating. ' In good faith as
for such Masses as he would have said, without the canon,
without the secrets, without oblation, without sacrifice,
without the body or blood of Christ, with bare signs and
tokens instead of the Blessed Sacrament ; I ween a woman
were indeed a more meet priest than St. Peter ' (E. W.,
p. 623, *misprinted* 563). And elsewhere in answer to a
similar claim made by Tyndale, at least in such cases of
necessity as a woman's being cast alone upon a pagan island,
More replies in words which have a special interest as coming
from the author of *Utopia*. ' Tyndale may make himself
sure that since there falleth not a sparrow upon the ground
without Our Father that is in heaven, there shall no woman
fall a-land in any so far an island, where He will have His
name preached, and His sacraments ministered, but that
God can, and will, well enough provide a man or twain to
come to land with her, whereof we have had already meetly
good experience, and that within few years. For I am sure
there have been more islands and more part of the firm
land and continent discovered and found out within this
forty years last passed ' (he is writing in 1532, forty years
after Columbus discovered America) ' than was new found,
as far as any man may perceive, this three thousand year
before, and in many of these places, the name of Christ new
known too, and preachings had, and sacraments ministered,
without any woman fallen a-land alone. But God hath
provided that His name is preached by such good Christian
folk as Tyndale now most raileth upon, that is, good religious
friars, and especially the Friars Observant, honest, godly,
chaste, virtuous people, not by such as Friar Luther is, that
is run out of religion, nor by casting a-land alone any such
holy nun as his harlot is.' (E. W., pp. 428–9.)

is not excluded from priesthood, howbeit few be
chosen, and none but widows and old women), the
men priests, I say, take to their wives[1] the chiefest
women in all their country. For to no office among
the Utopians is more honour and pre-eminence
given. Insomuch that if they commit any offence,
they be under no common judgment,[2] but be left

[1] *priests . . . take to their wives.* There was no reason why
Utopian priests, not being Christians, should not marry, any
more than Jewish priests. It is, however, a universal law
of the Church that priests may not marry after ordination,
though in many places in the near East married men may be
ordained priests. The distinction is not always noticed,
but More knew it well enough. Speaking of Greece, he says
in his *Dialogue* : ' Though a wedded man taken there into
the clergy be not nor cannot be put from his wife, but is
there suffered to minister in the office of a priest, notwithstanding his marriage ; yet, if he be unmarried at the
time that he taketh priesthood, he then professeth perpetual
continence, and never marrieth after.' (E. W., p. 231.)

More, then, did not object to married priests as such,
but to the breaking of vows. ' Since that chastity promised
once to God . . . hath always been . . . among Christians . . .
so highly esteemed, that the breakers thereof have always
been, by the common consent of the whole world . . . reputed
and punished as abominable wicked wretches, is it not now a
wondrous thing to see . . . now a lewd friar (Luther) so bold
and so shameless to marry a nun and bide thereby, and be
taken still for a Christian man and, over that, for a man
meet to be the beginner of a sect whom any honest man
should vouchsafe to follow ' (*ibid.*, p. 261).

[2] *under no common judgment.* Few matters have occasioned
more bitter quarrels between Church and State than the
privilege of the clergy to be exempt from the civil courts
and to be judged by their own ecclesiastical judges. It was
one of the principal points in the dispute which led to the
martyrdom of More's patron, St. Thomas of Canterbury.
Yet Hythloday makes even the pagan Utopians adopt it as a
most reasonable custom.

only to God and themselves. For they think it
not lawful to touch him with man's hand, be he
never so vicious, which after so singular a sort was
dedicated and consecrated to God as a holy offering.

This manner may they easily observe, because
they have so few priests, and do choose them with
such circumspection. For it scarcely ever chanceth
that the most virtuous among virtuous, which in
respect only of his virtue is advanced to so high a
dignity, can fall to vice and wickedness. And if it
should chance indeed (as man's nature is mutable
and frail), yet by reason they be so few, and
promoted to no might nor power but only to
honour, it were not to be feared that any great
damage by them should happen and ensue to the
commonwealth. They have so rare and few priests,
lest if the honour were communicated to many, the
dignity of the order, which among them now is so
highly esteemed, should run in contempt. Specially
because they think it hard to find many so good as
to be meet for that dignity, to the execution and
discharge whereof it is not sufficient to be endued
with mean virtues.[1]

Furthermore these priests be not more esteemed
of their own countrymen than they be of foreign
and strange countries. Which thing may hereby
plainly appear. And I think also that this is the

[1] *not sufficient to be endued with mean virtues.* This Utopian
view is in the fullest accord with Catholic teaching concerning the priesthood. More will have read in St. Thomas
Aquinas : ' For the due exercise of (holy) orders no ordinary
goodness is sufficient, but exceeding great holiness is essential :
so that as those who are ordained are by their rank raised
above the people, so may they be also by their sanctity.'
(*Suppl.*, Q. XXXV, a. 1.)

cause of it. For whilst the armies be fighting together in open field, they a little beside, not far off, kneel upon their knees in their hallowed vestments, holding up their hands[1] to heaven; praying first of all for peace, next for victory of their own part, but to neither part a bloody victory. If their host get the upper hand, they run into the main battle and restrain their own men from slaying and cruelly pursuing their vanquished enemies. Which enemies, if they do but see them and speak to them, it is enough for the safeguard of their lives. And the touching of their clothes[2] defendeth and saveth all their goods from ravin and spoil.

This thing hath advanced them to so great worship and true majesty among all nations, that many times they have as well preserved their own citizens from the cruel force of their enemies, as they have their enemies from the furious rage[3] of

---

[1] *holding up their hands*. More must surely have been thinking of *Exodus* xvii, 10. 'Josue . . . fought against Amalec, but Moses and Aaron and Hur went up upon the top of the hill. And when Moses lifted up his hands, Israel overcame . . . and Aaron and Hur stayed up his hands on both sides. And it came to pass that his hands were not weary until sunset.'

[2] *touching of their clothes*. The Utopians had thus something like the right of sanctuary—another ground of frequent dispute between Church and State in the Middle Ages.

[3] *their enemies from the furious rage*. No doubt More had in mind the very different behaviour of only too many Churchmen, e.g. the warlike Julius II, or the Archbishop of St. Andrews and others who fell at Flodden Field not long before he wrote the *Utopia*. But of this matter he would no doubt have said, as he said 'touching the choice of priests, I could not well devise better provisions than are by the laws of the Church provided already, if they were as well kept as they be well made' (E. W., p. 228). Council

their own men. For it is well known that, when their own army hath recoiled, and in despair turned back, and run away, their enemies fiercely pursuing with slaughter and spoil, then the priests coming between have stayed the murder, and parted both the hosts. So that peace hath been made and concluded between both parties upon equal and indifferent conditions. For there was never any nation, so fierce, so cruel, and rude, but they had them in such reverence, that they counted their bodies hallowed and sanctified, and therefore not to be violently and unreverently touched.

They keep holy the first and the last day of every month and year, dividing the year into months, which they measure by the course of the moon, as they do the year by the course of the sun. The first days they call in their language Lynemernes,[1]

after council raised its voice against the abuse. Two examples may be taken from the *Corpus Juris* (Decr. 2ª Pars, Causa XXIII, Q. 8). ' Clerics, who have taken up arms voluntarily in any sedition, or shall take them up, being so found, shall be degraded from their order and sent to a monastery to do penance' (Fourth Council of Toledo). Again, ' Clerics are not to take up weapons, nor to go about armed, but to honour the name they bear by religious behaviour and the religious dress. If they do not observe this rule, they are to be punished by degradation, for their contempt of the sacred canons and their profanation of ecclesiastical holiness, because they cannot be at the same time soldiers both of God and of the world.' (Council of Meaux.)

[1] *Lynemernes.* More wrote Cynemernos which Dr. Lupton thinks to be derived from κύων, dog, and ἡμέρα, day, and to signify the night between the old month and the new, when food was placed at the cross-roads, and the barking of the dogs was assumed to be a sign of the approach of Hecate. Robinson may have thought the word to be connected with ' Luna,' the moon, but that is Latin, not Greek.

and the last Trapemernes,[1] the which words may
be interpreted, primifeast and finifeast, or else in
our speech, first feast and last feast.

Their churches be very gorgeous, and not only
of fine and curious workmanship, but also (which
in the fewness of them was necessary) very wide
and large, and able to receive a great company of
people. But they be all somewhat dark.[2] Howbeit
that was not done through ignorance in building,
but as they say, by the counsel of the priests.
Because they thought that overmuch light doth
disperse men's cogitations, whereas in dim and
doubtful light they be gathered together, and more
earnestly fixed upon religion and devotion ; which
because it is not there of one sort among all men,
and yet all the kinds and fashions of it, though
they be sundry and manifold, agree together in the
honour of the divine nature, as going divers ways
to one end, therefore nothing is seen nor heard in
the churches, but that seemeth to agree indifferently
with them all. If there be a distinct kind of sacrifice
peculiar to any several sect, that they execute at
home in their own houses. The common sacrifices
be so ordered, that they be no derogation nor
prejudice to any of the private sacrifices[3] and
religions.

Therefore no image of any god is seen in the
church, to the intent it may be free for every man

[1] *Trapemernes* is from τρέπειν to turn, and means, no
doubt, the turning or closing-day. (Lupton.)

[2] *somewhat dark*. This seems unfair to the sun-worshippers.
See the beginning of the chapter.

[3] *sacrifices*. The original is *sacrum* which means any
sacred rite.

to conceive God by their religion after what likeness
and similitude they will. They call upon no peculiar
name of God, but only Mithra.[1] In the which
word they all agree together in one nature of the
divine majesty whatsoever it be. No prayers be
used but such as every man may boldly pronounce
without the offending of any sect.

They come therefore to the church, the last day
of every month and year, in the evening yet fasting,[2]
there to give thanks to God for that they have
prosperously passed over the year or month,
whereof that holy day is the last day. The next
day they come to the church early in the morning,
to pray to God that they may have good fortune
and success all the new year or month which they
do begin of that same holy day. But in the holy
days that be the last days of the months and years,
before they come to the church, the wives fall
down prostrate before their husband's feet at
home, and the children before the feet of their
parents, confessing and acknowledging themselves
offenders either by some actual deed, or by omission
of their duty, and desire pardon for their offence.
Thus if any cloud of privy displeasure was risen at
home, by this satisfaction it is overblown, that they
may be present at the sacrifices with pure and
charitable minds. For they be afraid to come there

[1] *Mithra.* As stated at the beginning of the chapter.
The common worship is reasonable enough, if it be practic-
able, where, in the absence of any divine revelation, it is
impossible to decide which form of religion is true.

[2] *fasting.* On an earlier page Hythloday made the Utopians
object to fasting (p. 156), but here he tells us they fast
according to the utmost rigour of the Church's ancient law
which forbade any food before sunset.

with troubled consciences. Therefore if they know themselves to bear any hatred or grudge towards any man, they presume not to come to the sacrifices, before they have reconciled themselves[1] and purged their consciences, for fear of great vengeance and punishment for their offence.

When they come thither, the men go into the right[2] side of the church, and the women into the left side. There they place themselves in such order, that all they which be of the male kind in every household sit before the goodman of the house, and they of the female kind before the goodwife. Thus it is foreseen that all their gestures and behaviours be marked and observed abroad of them by whose authority and discipline they be governed at home. This also they diligently see unto, that the younger evermore be coupled with his elder, lest children being joined together, they should pass over that time in childish wantonness, wherein they ought principally to conceive a religious and devout fear towards God; which is the chief and almost the only incitation to virtue.

---

[1] *before they have reconciled themselves.* This is in accordance with Our Lord's words : 'If thou offerest thy gift at the altar, and there shalt remember that thy brother hath anything against thee ; leave there thy gift before the altar and go first to be reconciled to thy brother, and then coming thou shalt offer thy gift.' (*Matt.* v, 23.)

[2] *men go into the right.* The separation of the sexes is a very ancient Christian custom and is still observed in many parts of the Catholic world. St. Augustine mentions it as part of his reply to the disgusting calumnies of the pagans against the Christians (*De Civ. Dei*, Book II, Chapter XXVIII).

They kill no living beast[1] in sacrifice, nor they
think not that the merciful clemency of God hath
delight in blood and slaughter, which hath given
life to beasts to the intent they should live. They
burn frankincense and other sweet savours, and
light also a great number of wax candles and tapers,
not supposing this gear to be anything available
to the divine nature, as neither the prayers of men.
But this unhurtful and harmless kind of worship
pleaseth them. And by these sweet savours and
lights, and other such ceremonies men feel themselves secretly lifted up, and encouraged to devotion
with more willing and fervent hearts. The people
weareth in the church white apparel. The priest
is clothed in changeable colours. Which in workmanship be excellent, but in stuff not very precious.
For their vestments be neither embroidered with
gold nor set with precious stones. But they be
wrought so finely and cunningly with divers
feathers of fowls, that the estimation of no costly
stuff is able to countervail the price of the work.
Furthermore in these birds' feathers, and in the
due order of them, which is observed in their
setting, they say, is contained certain divine
mysteries. The interpretation whereof known,

[1] *They kill no living beast*. But yet they had sacrifices
(see above p. 216), perhaps libations like the Greeks, or even
the sacrifices of bread and wine like Melchisedech (*Gen.* xiv,
18). We may compare the words of Isaias, ' To what purpose
do you offer me the multitude of your victims, saith the
Lord ? I am full, I desire not holocausts of rams, and fat
of fatlings, and blood of calves, and lambs, and buck goats '
(i, 11). Or the words of the Psalmist, ' With burnt offerings
thou wilt not be delighted : a sacrifice to God is an afflicted
spirit ' (l, 18).

which is diligently taught by the priests, they be put in remembrance of the bountiful benefits of God toward them; and of the love and honour which of their behalf is due to God; and also of their duties one toward another.

When the priest first cometh out of the vestry thus apparelled, they fall down incontinent every one reverently to the ground, with so still silence on every part, that the very fashion of the thing striketh into them a certain fear of God, as though He were there personally present. When they have lain a little space on the ground,[1] the priest giveth them a sign for to rise. Then they sing praises unto God, which they intermix with instruments of music, for the most part of other fashions than these that we use in this part of the world. And like as some of ours be much sweeter than theirs, so some of theirs do far pass ours. But in one thing doubtless they go exceeding far beyond us. For all their music both that they play upon instruments, and that they sing with man's voice, doth so resemble and express natural affections, the sound and tune is so applied and made agreeable to the thing, that whether it be a prayer, or else a ditty of gladness, of patience, of trouble, of mourning, or of anger, the fashion of the melody doth so represent the meaning of the thing, that it doth wonderfully move, stir, pierce, and inflame the hearers' minds.

At the last the people and the priest together rehearse solemn prayers in words, expressly pronounced, so made that every man may privately

---

[1] *lain a little space on the ground*. Like the ancient Christian custom, still observed by the ministers on Good Friday.

apply to himself that which is commonly spoken of all. In these prayers every man recogniseth and knowledgeth God to be his maker, his governor, and the principal cause of all other goodness, thanking Him for so many benefits received at His hand. But namely that through the favour of God he hath chanced into that public weal which is most happy and wealthy, and hath chosen that religion which he hopeth to be most true. In the which thing if he do anything err, or if there be any other better than either of them is, being more acceptable to God, he desireth Him that He will of His goodness let him have knowledge thereof, as one that is ready to follow[1] what way soever He will lead him. But if this form and fashion of a commonwealth be best, and his own religion most true and perfect, then he desireth God to give him a constant steadfastness in the same, and to bring all other people to the same order of living, and to the same opinion of God; unless there be anything that in this diversity of religions doth delight His unsearchable pleasure. To be short he prayeth Him, that after his death[2] he may come to Him. But how soon or late that he dare not assign or determine.

[1] *ready to follow*, etc. This important passage emphasises the principle that is essential to a right understanding of the *Utopia*, viz. that the customs of the island are based on purely natural reason, not on revealed truth. More points to the readiness of the Utopians to accept revealed religion, i.e. the Christian faith, as another proof of their natural goodness.

[2] *after his death*. The translation is inadequate. The prayer is, according to the Latin, that the Utopian may have an easy passage out of this world and a welcome from God, like the *Noctem quietam et finem perfectum* of Compline.

Howbeit, if it might stand with His majesty's pleasure, he would be much gladder to die[1] a painful death and so to go to God, than by long living in worldly prosperity to be away from Him. When this prayer is said they fall down to the ground again and a little after they rise up and go to dinner. And the residue of the day they pass over in plays,[2] and exercise of chivalry.

Now I have declared and described unto you, as truly as I could, the form and order of that commonwealth, which verily in my judgment is not only the best, but also that which alone of good right may claim and take upon it the name of a commonwealth or public weal. For in other places they speak still of the commonwealth. But every man procureth his own private gain. Here where nothing is private, the common affairs be earnestly looked upon. And truly on both parts they have good cause so to do as they do. For in other countries who knoweth not that he shall starve for hunger, unless he make some several provision for himself, though the commonwealth flourish never so much in riches? And therefore he is compelled even of very necessity to have regard to himself, rather than to the people, that is to say, to others.

[1] *gladder to die.* More constantly recurs to this theme. Thus in the *Dialogue of Comfort* he writes : ' He that so loveth Him that he longeth to go to Him, my heart cannot give me but he shall be welcome, all were it so that he should come ere he were well purged. . . But if God give the occasion that with His good will we may go, let us be glad thereof, and long to go to Him ' (p. 74. See also above p. 204).

[2] *plays*, i.e. games. The Utopians did not anticipate the gloomy Puritan Sunday.

Contrariwise there where all things be common
to every man, it is not to be doubted that any man
shall lack anything necessary for his private uses,
so that the common storehouses and barns be
sufficiently stored. For there nothing is distributed
after a niggardish sort, neither there is any poor
man or beggar. And though no man have anything,
yet every man is rich. For what can be more rich
than to live joyfully and merrily, without all grief
and pensiveness, not caring for his own living, nor
vexed or troubled with his wife's importunate
complaints,¹ nor dreading poverty to his son, nor
sorrowing for his daughter's dowry? Yea they take
no care at all for the living and wealth of themselves and all theirs, of their wives, their children,
their nephews, their children's children, and all the
succession that ever shall follow in their posterity.
And yet besides this there is no less provision for
them that were once labourers, and be now weak
and impotent, than for them that do now labour
and take pain.

Here now would I see, if any man dare be so
bold as to compare with this equity, the justice of
other nations. Among whom, I forsake God,² if
I can find any sign or token of equity and justice.
For what justice is this, that a rich goldsmith, or

¹ *wife's importunate complaints.* Compare the grim picture
More draws in ' The Four Last Things ' of a dying man
surrounded by relatives asking what they shall have of his
estate. ' Then shall come thy children and cry for their
parts. Then shall come thy sweet wife, and where in thine
health haply she spake thee not one sweet word in six weeks,
now shall she call thee sweet husband, and weep with much
work, and ask thee what she shall have ' (E. W., p. 78).

² *I forsake God.* Literally ' May I perish.'

an usurer,[1] or, to be short, any of them, which
either do nothing at all, or else that which they
do is such that it is not very necessary to the
commonwealth, should have a pleasant and a
wealthy living, either by idleness, or by unnecessary
business ; when in the meantime poor labourers,
carters, ironsmiths, carpenters, and ploughmen, by
so great and continual toil, as drawing and bearing
beasts be scant able to sustain, and again so necessary
toil, that without it no commonwealth were able to
continue and endure one year, should yet get so
hard and poor a living, and live so wretched and
miserable a life, that the state and condition of the
labouring beasts may seem much better and
wealthier ? For they be not put to so continual
labour, nor their living is not much worse, yea
to them much pleasanter, taking no thought in the
mean season for the time to come. But these silly
poor wretches be presently tormented with barren
and unfruitful labour. And the remembrance of
their poor indigent and beggarly old age killeth
them up. For their daily wages is so little,[2] that
it will not suffice for the same day, much less it
yieldeth any overplus that may daily be laid up
for the relief of old age.

[1] *goldsmith or an usurer*, i.e. those who lend money.
Banking, as Dr. Lupton remarks, was not a distinct occupation in England until after the Restoration.

[2] *daily wages is so little*. Compare the burning words of
Leo XIII in his *Encyclical on the Condition of the Working Classes*
(1891) : ' Wages ought not to be insufficient to support a frugal
and well-behaved wage-earner. If through necessity . . . a
workman accept harder conditions . . . he is made the victim
of force or injustice.' The Holy Father goes on to show that
the wages should be sufficient to enable him to support wife
and family and to put aside something for his old age.

R

Is not this an unjust and an unkind public weal, which giveth great fees and rewards to gentlemen, as they call them, and to goldsmiths, and to such other, which be either idle persons, or else only flatterers and devisers of vain pleasures ; and of the contrary part maketh no gentle provision for poor ploughmen, colliers, labourers, carters, ironsmiths, and carpenters, without whom no commonwealth can continue ? But after it hath abused the labours of their lusty and flowering age, at the last when they be oppressed with old age and sickness, being needy, poor, and indigent of all things, then forgetting their so many painful watchings, not remembering their so many and so great benefits, recompenseth and acquitteth them most unkindly with miserable death. And yet besides this the rich men not only by private fraud, but also by common laws, do every day pluck and snatch away from the poor some part of their daily living. So whereas it seemed before unjust to recompense with unkindness their pains that have been beneficial to the public weal, now they have to this their wrong and unjust dealing (which is yet a much worse point) given the name of justice, yea and that by force of a law.

Therefore, when I consider and weigh in my mind all these commonwealths which nowadays anywhere do flourish, so God help me, I can perceive nothing but a certain conspiracy of rich men[1] procuring their own commodities under the

---

[1] *conspiracy of rich men.* Compare the words of Leo XIII : ' A small number of very rich men have been able to lay upon the teeming masses of the labouring poor a yoke little better than that of slavery itself ' (*ibid.*).

name and title of the commonwealth. They invent
and devise all means and crafts, first how to keep
safely without fear of losing that they have unjustly
gathered together, and next how to hire and abuse
the work and labour of the poor for as little money
as may be. These devices, when the rich men have
decreed to be kept and observed under colour of
the commonalty, that is to say, also of the poor
people, then they be made laws.

But these most wicked and vicious men, when
they have by their unsatiable covetousness divided
among themselves all those things, which would
have sufficed all men, yet how far be they from the
wealth and felicity of the Utopian commonwealth ?
Out of the which, in that all the desire of money
with the use thereof is utterly secluded and banished,
how great a heap of cares is cut away ! How great
an occasion of wickedness and mischief is plucked
up by the roots ! For who knoweth not that fraud,
theft,[1] ravin, brawling, quarrelling, brabbling, strife,
chiding, contention, murder, treason, poisoning,
which by daily punishments are rather revenged
than refrained, do die when money dieth ? And
also that fear, grief, care, labours, and watchings
do perish even the very same moment that money
perisheth ? Yea poverty itself, which only seemed
to lack money, if money were gone, it also would
decrease and vanish away.

And that you may perceive this more plainly,
consider with yourselves some barren and unfruitful
year, wherein many thousands of people have

[1] *fraud*, *theft*, etc. ' Covetousness is the root of all evils'
(1 *Tim*. vi, 10). Compare an article in the *Month*, July, 1931,
p. 55.

starved for hunger. I dare be bold to say, that in
the end of that penury so much corn or grain
might have been found in the rich men's barns, if
they had been searched, as being divided among
them whom famine and pestilence then consumed,
no man at all should have felt that plague and
penury. So easily might men get their living, if
that same worthy princess Lady Money did not
alone stop up the way between us and our living,
which in God's name, was very excellently devised
and invented, that by her the way thereto should
be opened. I am sure the rich men perceive this,
nor they be not ignorant how much better it were
to lack no necessary thing, than to abound with
overmuch superfluity ; to be rid out of innumerable
cares and troubles, than to be besieged and encumbered with great riches.

And I doubt not that either the respect of every
man's private commodity, or else the authority of
our Saviour Christ (which for His great wisdom
could not but know what were best, and for His
inestimable goodness could not but counsel to that
which He knew to be best) would have brought all
the world long ago into the laws of this weal public,
if it were not that one only beast, the princess and
mother of all mischief, Pride,[1] doth withstand and

---

[1] *pride*. Holy Scripture brings together the two vices,
covetousness and pride. E.g. ' What hath pride profited us,
or what advantage hath the boasting of riches brought us ? '
(*Wisdom* v, 8). ' Nothing is more wicked than the covetous
man. Why is earth and ashes proud ? . . . Pride is the
beginning of all sin ' (*Ecclus*. x, 9, 15). More writes of both
vices in ' The Four Last Things,' and as the marginal notes
indicate, ' Pride the mother of all vice,' ' Covetous men be
proud,' he makes the same points as in the *Utopia* (E. W.,
pp. 82 and 92).

let it. She measureth not wealth and prosperity by her own commodities, but by the misery and incommodities of others, she would not by her goodwill be made a goddess, if there were no wretches left, over whom she might, like a scornful lady, rule and triumph, over whose miseries her felicities might shine, whose poverty she might vex, torment, and increase by gorgeously setting forth her riches. This hellhound creepeth into men's hearts, and plucketh them back from entering the right path of life, and is so deeply rooted[1] in men's breasts that she cannot be plucked out.

This form and fashion of a weal public, which I would gladly wish unto all nations, I am glad yet that it hath chanced to the Utopians, who have followed those institutions of life, whereby they have laid such foundations of their commonwealth, as shall continue and last not only wealthily, but also, as far as man's wit may judge and conjecture, shall endure for ever. For, seeing the chief causes of ambition and sedition, with other vices, be plucked up by the roots, and abandoned at home, there can be no jeopardy of domestic dissension which alone hath cast under foot and brought to naught the well-fortified and strongly defended wealth and riches of many cities. But forasmuch as perfect concord remaineth, and wholesome laws be executed at home, the envy of all foreign princes be not able to shake or move the empire, though they have

---

[1] *so deeply rooted*, etc. This sentence is a very free rendering of *velut remora retrahit et remoratur* and obscures the reference to the *remora*, the tiny fish of ancient fable which by fixing itself on to the hull was able to bring even the largest ship to a standstill.

many times long ago gone about to do it, being evermore driven back.

Thus when Raphael had made an end of his tale, though many things came to my mind which in the manners and laws of that people seemed to be instituted and founded of no good reason, not only in the fashion of their chivalry, and in their sacrifices and religions, and in other of their laws, but also, yea, and chiefly, in that which is the principal foundation of all their ordinances, that is to say, in the community of their life and living, without any occupying of money, by the which thing only all nobility, magnificence, worship, honour, and majesty, the true ornaments and honours, as the common opinion is,[1] of a commonwealth, utterly be overthrown and destroyed; yet because I knew that he was weary of talking, and was not sure whether he could abide that anything should be said against his mind; specially remembering that he had reprehended this fault in others, which be afraid lest they should seem not to be wise enough, unless they could find some fault in other men's inventions; therefore I praising both their institutions and his communication, took him by the hand, and led him in to supper, saying that we would choose another time to weigh and examine the same matters, and to talk with him more at large therein. Which would God it might once come to pass. In the meantime, as I cannot

---

[1] *as the common opinion is.* No doubt there is sarcasm here, the true ornaments of a state being justice and good government, yet it is noteworthy that More's last word, spoken in his own person, is 'I cannot agree and consent to all things that he said.'

agree and consent to all things that he said, being else without doubt a man singularly well learned, and also in all worldly matters exactly and profoundly experienced; so must I needs confess and grant that many things be in the Utopian weal public which in our cities I may rather wish for than hope after.

THUS ENDETH THE AFTERNOON'S TALK OF RAPHAEL HYTHLODAY CONCERNING THE LAWS AND INSTITUTIONS OF THE ISLAND OF UTOPIA.

A METRE OF FOUR VERSES IN THE UTOPIAN TONGUE

Briefly touching as well the strange beginning as also the happy and wealthy continuance of the same commonwealth

UTOPOS ha Boccas peula chama polta chamaan.
Bargol he maglomi baccan soma gynmnosophaon.
Agrama gymnosophon labarem bacha bodamilomin.
Voluala barchin heman la lauoluala dramme pagloni.

Which verses the translator, according to his simple knowledge, and mean understanding in the Utopian tongue, hath thus rudely Englished.[1]

My king and conqueror Utopus by name,
A prince of much renown and immortal fame,
Hath made me an isle that erst no island was,
Full fraught with worldly wealth, with pleasure and
    solace.
I, one of all other without philosophy,
Have shaped for man a philosophical city.
As mine I am nothing dangerous to impart,
So better to receive I am ready with all my heart.

[1] Translation from edition of 1555.

a b c d e f g h i k l m n o p q r s t u x y

◐⊖⊙⊕⊖⊙⊋ℂⵙⵕⵎⵥ△⌐⌐⊡⊞⊞⊟⊟

TETRASTICHON VERNACVLA VTO-
PIENSIVM LINGVA.

Vtopos ha Boccas peula chama.

polta chamaan

Bargol he maglomi baccan

foma gymnofophaon

Agrama gymnofophon labarem

bacha bodamilomin

Voluala barchin heman la

lauoluola dramme pagloni.

HORVM VERSVVM AD VERBVM HAEC
EST SENTENTIA.

Vtopus me dux ex non infula fecit infulam.
Vna ego terrarum omnium abfq; philofophia,
Ciuitatem philofophicam expreffi mortalibus.
Libenter impartio mea, non grauatim accipio meliora.

b 3

A SHORT METRE OF UTOPIA[1]

written by Anemolius,[2] *poet laureate, and nephew
to Hythloday by his sister*

ME Utopie cleped Antiquity,
   Void of haunt and herboroughe,[3]
Now am I like to Plato's city,
Whose fame flieth the world through.
Yea like, or rather more likely
Plato's plat to excel and pass.
For what Plato's pen hath platted[4] briefly
In naked words, as in a glass,
The same have I performed fully,
With laws, with men, and treasure fitly.
Wherefore not Utopie, but rather rightly
My name is Eutopie : a place of felicity.

---

[1] Translation from edition of 1556.
[2] From ἄνεμος, the wind, and thus 'a gas-bag.'
[3] lodging.   [4] sketched.

INDEX